Little Adventures in Yemen

Absolutely (Un)True Stories from Sana'a

by FRANCA SOL

Illustrations by SARAH ALJOUMARI

جلسة

ARTS & CULTURE

YEME
Sa'dah
صعدة
الجوف
Aljawf
صنعاء
Sana'a
Hajjah
Ma'
مأرب
شبوة
ريمة
Shabwah
Ibb
عدن
أبين
Aden
Abyan
تعز
Ta'izz
Gulf of Ade
Bab almandab

Little Adventures in Yemen

Absolutely (Un)True Stories from Sana'a

by FRANCA SOL

Illustrations by SARAH ALJOUMARI

Disclaimer: This book is (not) based on a true story.
Any resemblance of the characters to real persons
is purely coincidental and unpredicted, as is
everything that happens in Yemen.

Copyright © 2020 Jalsa Arts & Culture. All rights reserved.
Book Design: Katarina Simkova
ISBN: 978-84-09-24398-3

CONTENTS

For Luke.

WELCOME TO
Yemen

Yemen is a very peculiar place. Mix chaos, poverty, strong traditions, tribes, and weapons ... et voila! You have it. But the fact is, Yemeni people are the most humble and good-hearted people on Earth. After years living there, I still found Yemen fascinating, unbelievable, surprising, annoying, and unique. The truth is, there was not a single day I didn't love and hate it, because Yemen gives you as much as it takes, and sometimes it takes a lot.

Adventure 1
MR. LOCAL

CHAPTER 1

When I first arrived in Yemen, I stayed away from drama for a whole year. My previous job was in Lebanon, where I worked hard and partied harder, meeting people who would become best friends, breaking hearts, and getting heartbroken. It was there I learned just how toxic drama can be. It only brings headaches, but let's admit it, it's also addictive. Very addictive.

When I landed in Yemen, I'd decided to put some distance between me and the past and focus exclusively on my new job, which involved working with a local organization to help counter human trafficking. It was challenging and exciting and after nearly twelve months, I felt confident that my time in Yemen was going to be drama-free.

On the eve of my 24th birthday, Bilma, my crazy Indian colleague, flat mate, and best friend, and Asrat, our Ethiopian neighbor, walked into Club Istanbul, the only night club in Yemen. Sak Noel's song, Paso filled the air around us. *Mama, there is no need for drama...* the words echoed my new motto. Like a tacky version of a Roman amphitheater, twelve sets of a crystal-buttoned purple sofas and low, mirrored tables created a semi-circle around the dance floor. Half-broken speakers pumped out DJ's selection of Reggaeton, Turkish hits, American pop and African beats. The bar was the testosterone-only area where hairy men occupied the zebra print barstools.

We took our places on our favorite sofa, decorated with birthday balloons for that night, overlooking the dance floor.

A man approached our table, and when he got close enough to see our faces, he made a sharp turn back to the bar. In my estimation, no drama meant no boys, and I'd already devised a strategy to deal with that. I was polite, but forceful in my rejections, so the regulars had long since stopped bothering with me. Bilma shared the same approach. Asrat, was the exception to my rule. He was known for livening up parties with his dance moves as his African compatriots cheered him on and he greeted everyone with a smile. The three of us made the perfect party team.

I smiled as I watched the man walk away. I was well on my way to keeping my promise to myself thanks to a strict policy of no crazy parties, no crazy people, and absolutely no men. The nuns from my primary school days would have been proud.

"Remind me again why you are 'on strike'," Bilma said, not for the first time. Asrat looked at me curiously.

"Mama, there is no need for drama..." I sang and laughed, avoiding the question. Their insistent gazes forced me to continue. "Guys, the past is past, and some closed doors are closed, not to be opened again. What is the point of talking about it?"

"At least tell us when you're going to break your strike," Asrat laughed.

"For sure not today, and probably not tomorrow," I said with a grin. "Let's go dance."

We danced until the early hours of the morning. I fell into bed as the sun was rising, the first day of my twenty-fourths. My eyes closed and I fell into a deep sleep, blissfully unaware that everything was about to change.

CHAPTER 2

I've always been a big fan of couchsurfing. The online community allows you to host travelers in your house or request to crash on a local couch when travelling. I find it is the perfect way of meeting local people and other expats abroad. I hosted lots of travelers in Lebanon and had planned to continue the tradition in Yemen by offering my couch to the worldwide couchsurfing community. Very few tourists ventured into Yemen, so I wasn't surprised when no one took me up on my offer. Then, after a year without a single request, I received a message from an Italian man who would be traveling to Yemen for a couple of days to close a business deal.

The man was afraid of staying in a hotel and assumed it would be safer and less conspicuous if he stayed in a local house. I was thrilled. I would be the first person ever to have a couchsurfer in the whole history of couchsurfing in Yemen (take that)! Straight away I posted a message in the forum. *Hey couchsurfers of Yemen! I'm hosting a guest from Italy starting day after tomorrow. It would be nice to take him out to taste delicious Yemeni tea and meet some Sana'anis. Anyone want to join? To my surprise, someone replied immediately. Yes, I would love to. I am Yemeni and I recently came back from abroad and already miss international people. I can show you both some nice local places.*

A few days later we met. Me, my couchsurfer, and Mr. Local. Our destination for tea was in the Old City, an ancient labyrinth of narrow streets lined with two-thousand-year-old mud houses. This was especially convenient, since it was also the neighborhood where I was living.

Mr. Local looked young, perhaps a few years younger than me. As we walked, he explained that he had been away at university in Malaysia and was now preparing for a four-month internship. He would return to Kuala Lumpur to finish his final year.

"Did you do a lot of couchsurfing in Malaysia?" I asked.

"I actually only just joined couchsurfing the same day you posted," he confessed. "The first post in the forum that I saw was your suggestion to meet."

Was it destiny? I wondered sarcastically. We were walking around the old souk and I was too busy explaining things to my guest to take much notice of the young man, but the more we walked, the more curious I became. What struck me the most was his beautiful shyness. He didn't have the kind of shyness that makes you suffer because you can feel the other person is having a bad time. No, his shyness was charming, a mixture of curious eyes and an easy smile. It felt to me like a little glimpse of the first layer of an incredible, good-hearted personality. After our tour, we sat in a typical street café at a long shared table. It's the kind of place where the loose table legs always move slightly and there are only dirty metal benches to sit on. They are my favorite places.

Mr. Local went to ask for tea and the Italian couchsurfer turned to me. "Be careful with this young one," he winked. "He'll be on the hunt for you."

"Come on, I could be his mum!" I laughed. It wasn't really true, he was only two years younger than me, but I liked to exaggerate, and my impression of him was almost maternal. I saw him as a nice young chap with his whole life in front of him and a lot of potential to offer the world. The Italian just shook his head. Mr. Local returned with our tea and suggested that we make a trip to the fish market the next day to buy some fresh shrimp for the couchsurfer's last dinner.

"In Yemen they have a very cool business concept: you can bring your own raw seafood to little fish restaurants that are meant just for this purpose," he explained.

"There is no menu, and whatever you bring, they will cook for you and charge you for the service. This is what we will do with our shrimp," I added. I wanted our guest to leave Yemen with a full stomach, a big smile, and a good impression of the country.

Mr. Local arrived to pick up Bilma, the couchsurfer, and me. His self-described 'gangsta' cousin sat in the driver's seat, and while we drove, Mr. Local acted as our official tour guide, explaining everything imaginable to our Italian guest. As he spoke, I noticed the same cute smile I'd tried to ignore the day before, and the same delicate look in his big green eyes. I also noticed that he was tall, with a strong body that contrasted with his porcelain doll features. I shook my head. I wasn't interested in pretty boys. Or any boys at all for that matter. The strike would continue.

We got enough shrimp for ten people and ate them directly from a shared plate in the center of our plastic table, scooping them up with our fingers and pieces of flatbread. After dinner, we leaned back in our plastic chairs and drank tea and told stories over the roar of the ceiling fan. I knew our guest would leave Yemen full and happy, just as I had hoped he would.

Over the next few weeks, Mr. Local became a regular visitor. He, Bilma, and I were always together, even for the most trivial things. A tea here, a potato sandwich there, a fish dinner on our terrace, a bit of qat chewing, a majlis pillow fight. There were no hidden intentions, we simply got along well and enjoyed each other's company. Then, one full-moon night, we found ourselves alone on my terrace.

A force seemed to pull at our souls, the attraction too strong to resist. Our lips met. Without me realizing it or wanting it, my strike was over.

We saw each other even more often, falling harder for one another with every day, every hour, every minute, every second we spent together. I didn't tell Bilma about the subtle, but important shift in my friendship with Mr. Local. I knew there would be time for that later and I just wanted to savor it.

One afternoon I sat on the couch thinking about where we might all go for dinner. Bilma was comfortably curled in front of her computer, sipping green tea. "I'm too curious. I just have to know," she said, snapping me out of my thoughts of fassoulia and grilled fish.

"To know what?" I asked.

"Today I'm going to ask Mr. Local about his fiancée," she said, still staring at her computer, completely oblivious to the ripple of shock waves her words had sent coursing through me.

"What fiancée? How do you know he has a fiancée?" I said, sitting up.

"His Facebook status, see..." she said, turning her screen towards me.

I stared at her, frozen. I didn't want to look down at the screen. I didn't want to believe what I was hearing. Maybe she had misread or misunderstood. My eyes dropped. There it was. Written in undeniable, black-and-white *English — Relationship Status: ENGAGED.*

Yemen is a patriarchal society in every sense, from P to L. Patriarchal, patrilineal, and any other patri-you might find. According to the Cambridge dictionary, a patriarchy is: *a society controlled by men in which they use their power to their own advantage* and, according to the Yemeni spoken dictionary, is defined as: *You women stay home and shut up.* This is basically the same definition without the British politeness. (Before you get all up in arms about the injustice of it all, think about it for a minute. Isn't it like that everywhere? Yes, you are completely right, it is.)

The tribe is the most important component of society. Everyone has a tribal affiliation. Thus, you belong to a tribe, which in turn belongs to a confederation of tribes. There are two main confederations, one of which is composed of a hundred tribes, each composed of thousands of families. This system of allegiances creates a delicate balance of power that keeps confrontation among tribes low. In fact, tribal law is used to solve most of the disputes happening in Yemen, from a simple goat robbery to murders or land disputes.

Any big decision is discussed by the important members of the tribe and if a solution cannot be found, the whole confederation will get involved in the discussion until a final decision is made. If the problem is among tribes from different confederations, the elders of each side will try to reach an agreement. Usually the agreement involves the payment of some money and donation of guns and cattle. For example, two million rial, 50 AK-47[*] and 20 goats. Nowadays, the system has been modernized, with 4 x 4 vehicles being offered in place of cattle and goats. Cash and AK-47s remain a standard part of the compensation package.

---

[*] Type of assault rifle manufactured in the former Soviet Union, also known as Kalashnikov, widely popular due to its easy use and reliability over time and harsh conditions.

In the cases where no agreement can be reached, the not-quite-elders enter a violent spiral in which armed confrontations can last for years with new generations inheriting old grudges that span four or five decades.

At the individual level, if they call you to meet, you go to the tribal gathering. If they need you, you are available, any time of day or night. They will decide who you marry, against whom you will fight, and even which food you will eat. Sounds harsh? Well, the whole point of tribal affiliation is that you may be at the tribe's beck and call, but they are also there as a permanent safety net. If you get in trouble, your tribe is there for you. If you don't have job, the tribe will find one for you. If you want to get married, they will provide you with a wife. If you have a daughter to marry off, they will find you a husband for her. It's like having Doraemon's pocket in real life.

Political parties mirror the tribal structure: one big tribe, one big party. Thus, it is the big tribal leaders who are the real bosses of the country. To the world they say:

Dear stupid Western countries, you who believe anything convenient for you, listen up — we are a multiparty democracy with no elections, so keep sending us dollars in foreign aid to help us build a democracy (and so our pockets keep on getting bigger). Love you, thanks!

To sum up the societal power structure of Yemen: women obey men, men obey tribe, tribes obey confederation of tribes, confederation of tribes rule in the shape of political parties.

CHAPTER 3

"**W**ow, yes, engaged..." I murmured to Bilma. E-N-G-A-G-E-D: One word with no room for self-deception or misunderstanding. But really? How could that be possible? He never mentioned anything about a girlfriend or fiancée whatsoever. It could be a way of keeping tiresome girls out of his life, right? What a stupid thought. And how stupid one's mind can be when you don't want to believe the most clear-cut facts. But humans survive through self-delusion, like a built-in mechanism to protect us from blowing our mental circuits. "It's on his Facebook, so ask him about it if you want." I smiled with my best poker face. "I'm going to get ready for dinner."

I was fuming by the time Mr. Local and his friend arrived at the house an hour later, but I kept my cool as I greeted the group and followed Bilma out the door. She and I walked behind the boys to a little street food stall down the block to order fresh mango juice before dinner. I knew Bilma would bring up the fiancé, it was only a matter of time. When something piqued her curiosity, she couldn't stop thinking about it. In this case, neither could I. We picked up our juices and sat at a small metal table, just in front of the shop.

"Mr. Local, you have a fiancée?" Bilma abruptly asked. I almost choked on my mango juice straw.

"Yes," he said without hesitation. "My family engaged me last year."

An awkward silence followed.

"So, tell me more," Bilma continued, unknowingly rubbing salt in my wound. "Is she Yemeni?"

"Yes," he said.

Cricket-cricket. Two more seconds of painful silence followed.

"From Sana'a," he finally slurred.

"How did you meet?" she cheerfully asked, blissfully unaware of the growing tension around the table. I wished the ground would swallow me up. Bilma enough! I wanted to shout. I don't want to hear any more, it is enough, I just want to disappear, disappear and disappear... I silently stared at my juice.

"I met her in primary school," he said, looking down at his hands. It was becoming obvious Mr. Local was feeling highly uncomfortable, so his friend (and this is a real friend, the one who saves your ass) jumped in.

"Hey guys! I shouldn't know all this! Talk about it another day when I'm not around," he said, laughing lightly. "You know, it is not allowed for me to ask about my friends' female relatives, sisters, wives...I guess a fiancée is in this category, too."

It was true. In Yemen men remain unaware of the first names of their friends' mothers, sisters, and wives as part of a rigorously implemented no-ask policy. That's part of the reason why ladies are called after their first son's name: Um Fahad (the mother of Fahad), Um Fuad (Fuad's mom), and happily use this moniker even when giving their names as they drop clothes off for cleaning at the laundry.

The conversation had been effectively terminated by the rescuer friend, so we quietly finished our juice and no mention was made of dinner. We arrived home and Mr. Local stopped me in the staircase as Bilma entered the house ahead of us. "Are you mad?" he asked

"I am...disappointed," I said. "Which is worse."

"I have never lied to you, it is something public, it is in my Facebook," he said pleadingly.

"But you never mentioned it," I said, growing angry. "Am I supposed to check your Facebook to know who you are?"

"I am sorry, but really, I never meant to hide it from you. I thought you knew..."

"Sincerely, I would have preferred to know it by your words. But, anyways, now I know," I said, turning away and walking towards the door. He couldn't add a single word more. He knew I was right. I turned back just in time to see his deeply sad green eyes. I shared his sadness. I watched as he disappeared into the fading light.

Everything I told you I was feeling was real, read the text message he sent later that night. I knew he meant it. I did not reply. Disappointment is worse than anger. Anger goes away fast, but disappointment silently sits in that little corner of your heart and stays there. I could not be with someone who already belonged to someone else. It wouldn't be fair. I was already feeling guilty for the time we had spent together, even without me knowing. I couldn't imagine how much worse I would have felt if I didn't stop after I did know.

But that was my mind talking. Heart and mind are best enemies, and my heart was putting up a fight. He didn't look happy at all when speaking about the engagement, I reasoned. It was definitely arranged... to deny affection to someone who has been forced to get engaged, and to yourself, is that fair? I decided to put distance between us and ignored the onslaught of messages, pictures, voice notes, songs, and emoticons he sent. I just wanted the flame to fizzle out. I wanted to listen to my mind, and get back to my comfortable, safe strike.

One Thursday afternoon, on the eve of a new weekend about to start*, I was still at work when my phone vibrated. It was Mr. Local. He was writing to offer me a rare opportunity: a weekend trip to the seaside town of Hudeidah. No, I am not seeing this message, I told myself, turning my phone over. Then my phone rang. Ignore. It rang again. I did not pick up. Bilma's Bollywood ringtone suddenly filled the office. She was sitting at the desk in front of me and when she raised her phone, I could see Mr. Local's name on the caller ID. Panic gripped me. Bilma didn't know anything about our broken love story and before I could think of an excuse to stop her, she had picked up. I looked around my desk frantically, picking up a piece of paper and scrawling: You do what you feel like doing. Feel free to join the trip, I still don't know if I will go. I held it up in front of her. I was definitely, 100% not going, but I didn't want to deny Bilma the chance to get outside of Sana'a and have some fun.

Bilma nodded as Mr. Local spoke, then she cut him off. "Thanks for the invite, I'll think about it and call you back," she said and hung up. She turned to look at me. "They are offering us a trip to Hudeidah, and I love the sea, but I already have other plans for the weekend. Too bad, right?" she said apologetically.

"It's fine, next time," I said, sighing with relief. I was safe. I left the office and walked towards our flat in the old city, putting the trip and everything related to Mr. Local out of my mind. I was ready for a relaxing weekend and a bit of dancing at Club Istanbul. I was starving by the time I walked in the door and went straight to the shared kitchen on the upper floor of the building to prepare

---

* In Yemen the weekend is Friday and Saturday. When I first started working, the weekend in the country used to be Thursday and Friday but the country changed it to facilitate business with international companies. Can you imagine sending an email Wednesday afternoon and only following up with the conversation on Monday? Not business-friendly at all!

a quick, sad salad of tuna and boiled eggs. I ate standing in the kitchen, dropping my dish in the sink before heading back downstairs.

When I entered the living room, I automatically checked my phone. One missed call from Mr. Local. Another one, a third one... how many times had he rung in ten minutes? Knock-knock, knock-knock, knock-knock-knock-knock! Someone was rapping loudly on my door. With phone in hand, I looked through the peephole. Mr. Local was standing in the corridor. Why was he there? He was supposed to be on the way to Hudeidah already. I stepped back from the door, wondering if I could ignore his knocks, but he was making so much noise. Neighbors in the old city love to gossip, and a man knocking desperately on my door was sure to bring me a hell lot of problems. I took a deep breath. I had no choice. I had to save the centuries' old door and my reputation. "Come inside," I hissed.

"I came for you, to bring you on this trip with me," he said as soon as we were inside. "Bilma called me and declined the invitation for the trip, but she didn't mention anything about you, so I couldn't go without knowing if you would have wanted to come with me," his words poured out. Breathe darling, breathe! I thought, cursing his cute, worried face. "Besides, it would be a wonderful opportunity for you to have a break and chill and go to the sea and relax from dusty Sana'a. So, I decided to come here and ask you directly."

KALASHNIKOVS
AND
Yoghurt

I was afraid of weapons when I arrived in Yemen. I wasn't used to seeing them and I didn't know anyone who owned one. They made me even more nervous in the hands of teenagers. Puberty and cockiness exist everywhere, but if you add a rifle to the mix, the combination can become pretty explosive. During my first weeks in Yemen, every time I'd see a man carrying a Kalashnikov on his back, I would walk to the other side of the street. I looked like a snake as I staggered back and forth. There were so many guns!

Walking in just that manner, I arrived at Hudda Supermarket, one of the few supermarkets in Sana'a. I was tired of the only option for yoghurt (and any other product) on offer at the little shops in my neighborhood. There, I had to ask for what I wanted, and with my poor knowledge of Arabic, it always took me hours to buy something as simple as bread and yoghurt — one brand, type, size, taste — take it or leave it.

I can eat one liter of yoghurt in a single sitting, so this was a hardship. Inspired by my love of cultured dairy, I set out that morning on an adventurous trip to "the" supermarket.

I entered the supermarket, which in any other part of the world would be considered a small-to-medium shop, and wandered down the aisles. When I reached the yoghurt fridge, I could barely contain my emotions. There were three different brands to choose from! Un-be-lievable. They were all half-liter, full-fat, plain yoghurt, but I still got to choose between brands. I wondered which one I should take. *Should I buy all three?* Blind with joy, I didn't notice the man next to me was also looking for yoghurt. I took a step backwards and I brushed against something cold. I turned and came face-to-face with a Kalashnikov hanging from his shoulder. My moment of bliss was destroyed. I quickly grabbed a yoghurt, paid the cashier, and ran out of the supermarket.

Safely out in the street, I looked down at my purchase. It was the same brand carried in the small shop next to my flat.

One of the amazing things about humans is how quickly we adapt to new environments. Just two months later, I returned to the same supermarket with a German consultant who had joined my organization. The supermarket was close to our office, so I went weekly to indulge in some imported Turkish cookies or chocolate and always a tub of my favorite brand of yoghurt. We were next in the register queue, when a man stepped in front of us and dropped his groceries in front of the cashier.

"Excuse me sir!" I exclaimed in my poor Arabic. "It is my turn now. Me, first." I added, in case he didn't understand my first attempt. The man glared at me and picked up his items, stepping back to let us pay for our goods.

"But you are crazy!" the German exclaimed as we walked out of the market. "Didn't you realize that guy was carrying a rifle?"

"Yes, I know. I saw it," I calmly replied.

"So? Do you want him to shoot at you and die for a container of yoghurt?"

"Look, if we waited until everyone with a weapon paid, we'd be waiting till tomorrow," I said with a shrug, taking a sip of my yoghurt walking straight back to the office without crossing the street.

CHAPTER 4

"**P**lease come, you have to trust me," Mr. Local pleaded. "I cannot trust you," I said.

"Please, only this once. You will not regret it," he begged.

His eyes were so sincere, they broke down my defenses. "Well..." I said, beginning to consider his offer. To travel in Yemen you need a bunch of permits issued by the tourist police, a special unit that deals with foreigners living in Yemen. You usually need to ask for these permits in advance and even in quiet times, they are usually denied. Actually, I think the word "denied" is the only word police officers need to learn in order to work in the tourist police department: denied, and its synonym, no. I want to go South. *No.* Can I go East? *No.* West? *No.* North? *No way.* Ok... then maybe center? *You are already in the center, Miss.* This would be the longest conversation you could possible hope to have with the police officers working in that unit. The one solution for ladies who want to travel within Yemen is to "go local" and wear niqab, the piece of clothing that totally covers the face, except for two little slits for the eyes. Neither the police nor the tribes would ever ask to see your face at either the legal (army) checkpoints or illegal (tribal) checkpoints on the road.

To have a local woman travelling in the car usually gives the driver a free pass. No officer would check the car or even dare to directly stare at the lady sitting inside. The occupants of the vehicle are assumed to be a family, the most holy institution in Yemen. No one wants to bother them. To stop them would be considered disrespectful. This is why local ladies have been increasingly involved in kidnappings. Having women in the car guarantees that no one will stop the car transporting the kidnapped person for more than five seconds, and typically they are simply waved through. There have even been cases in which kidnapped men were dressed up as local ladies to make them easier to smuggle through checkpoints.

If you are a lady and want to travel, forget permits, buy a *niqab*. It's in fashion for every season, the Zorro eye-mask will always spare you problems and it pairs perfectly with Batman capes *yaani abbayas*. That said, not a lot of Yemenis dare to travel with a foreigner, especially a woman. If they were discovered, they could easily be accused of immorality or even attempted kidnapping. There are also the logistical issues. When you travel in Yemen as a foreigner, you need to show your travelling permits at any hotel you want to stay in. If you are (or are pretending to be) a local, you have to show your marriage certificate if you are traveling with your husband or your family book if you are traveling with your father. Ladies are absolutely not allowed to travel alone (lest you get lost!). If you are a young, local, unmarried man, like Mr. Local, and someone sees you travelling with a young lady, your reputation will be ruined. You will bring shame and embarrassment to your family, which, in Yemen, is the worst thing that can happen. It is what the nuns from my primary school would call "Completely. Unacceptable. Behavior." With a two-second pause between each word.

How could I say no to those pleading eyes, given the fact that Mr. Local was ready to take that kind of risk just to take me to a seaside town six hours from Sana'a? I packed pajamas, a couple of t-shirts, a couple of *abbayas*, my swimming suit, and a new *niqab* I'd never worn before. I took a seat in the back of the car. Two of Mr. Local's friends, who I'd never met, sat in the other seats. We pulled away from my flat and Mr. Local's friends offered me some qat, the national drug of Yemen, which I politely refused. I wondered for a moment if I was crazy to take this trip.

We flew past the last Sana'a army checkpoint about 12 kilometers outside of the city and were officially outside of the area I was allowed to move freely in without a permit. I awkwardly pulled on my Zorro eye-mask for first time. I'd tried on the *niqabs* of my colleagues before, but only for a few seconds. Mr. Local's friend who sat next to me, politely explained how to wear it the Yemeni way. "The eye fringe, the part that remains open, it has to finish before eyebrows. Eyebrows must be completely cover," he said. "Top one has to go up to veil start. No line between two pieces. Like engineering, no?" he laughed.

We slowed down as we approached the first checkpoint. I could feel the tension in the car. I tried not to look directly at the soldier. It was a western habit that I indulged in back in Sana'a, but ladies in Yemen avoid eye contact with men at all times, especially in public places and when speaking to men who are not their relatives. To look directly into the eyes of a man makes people think a woman is trying to flirt, to be seen, to catch attention. It's considered indecent, and ladies who behave that way are treated as such.

The soldier waved us through and we let out a collective sigh of relief. The young man next to me became talkative and smiley. Mr. Local sat in front, acting as copilot to the serious-looking young driver. I learned they had all studied together in Malaysia on government scholarships given to the best high school students each year. They had returned to Sana'a together for their internships and were looking forward to returning to Kuala Lumpur at the end of the summer. They were nice. I wasn't surprised. Mr. Local was a good guy, so why shouldn't his friends be, too?

Despite our smooth journey, I began to question my decision to come along. *What am I doing here? He has a fiancée. This is a terrible idea. I'm stuck for three days with him and two other boys I don't even know.* My thoughts spiraled on a closed loop. We were waved through another army checkpoint where I applied the same look-down-not-at-the-soldier strategy. We had officially entered tribal land. For the next few hours, every thirty to forty minutes we crossed a new tribal checkpoint, each one marking the entrance to or exit of a new territory. Tribal checkpoints are usually the ones foreigners are afraid of, and with good reason, but since we were travelling under the family label, they were the easiest for us to navigate. Since some local ladies do not talk at all to non-relative men, Mr. Local had given me his sister's ID card and told me to stay quiet and simply pull the ID out of my purse and show it to whoever asked me questions at the checkpoint.

By the fourth checkpoint, we had grown confident. I learned that the driver was married and on his way to visit his wife and children who were living in a village a couple of hours from our seaside destination. The plan was to drop him off with his family and continue to Hudeidah with his car. Though he was younger than the rest of us, only 22, he had married a 16-year-old girl when he was 19, a year after his father died. He now had a little boy and a very cute little girl. He turned out to be clever, charming, and completely committed to the wellbeing of his family. It was difficult for him to study and be away from them, but he was doing so to give them a better future.

We dropped the driver off in his village and Mr. Local took the wheel. The last few hours of our six-hour drive were breathtaking. Sana'a is located more than 2000 meters above the sea level and is surrounded by mountains, so to get out of the capital, first you need to drive even higher into the

Haraz Mountains before descending down a dangerously curvy mountain road. At the bottom, a new world awaits. The green mountain bushes disappear into a flat, sandy color desert that runs straight into the sea. You can see the ocean on the horizon for hours before actually reaching it. Then, like a mirage taking shape, the crystal calm water spreads out before you.

We pulled into Hudeidah just as the sun was beginning to set. Though pretending to be Mr. Local's sister worked at the checkpoints, it wasn't going to get us into a hotel. A man doesn't bring his sister to a hotel, especially if a male friend is also travelling with him. If we wanted to sleep under a roof that night, we would need a new strategy. We decided to pretend I was Mr. Local's wife, a role I was deeply delighted by, though I tried not to show it. We approached the counter of the run-down motel. And Mr. Local spoke in hushed tones to the attendant. "Yes sir, I understand, but I need the marriage certificate if you want a room in this hotel. I cannot do anything without it," the man said apologetically.

We tried a hotel a few blocks away, with the same result. At the third hotel, we decided I would pretend to be his sister. "Absolutely, we have many rooms available," the man at the desk smiled. "Just fill out this form and we will make a photocopy of your ID and family book. We stood in front of the hotel, defeated.

"You can go to the Sana'a airport and take a national flight with a fake ID and no one will notice, but try to get a room in a hotel without the marriage certificate and you'll end up sleeping in a prison?" I complained.

Mr. Local's phone rang. The driver had called to check on us. I listened as Mr. Local explained our situation. He began to smile, thanked him, and hung up. "His uncle is from this area, and he has a friend who owns a hostel," he said.

"He is going to call him and tell him we are newlyweds on our honeymoon, but we are still waiting for our marriage certificate. Since he knows the guy, and his family has a good reputation, he doesn't think the man will ask any questions." I nodded. In Yemen, it would be shameful to ask someone you trust for evidence of what he is saying. And no one would expect him to lie about something like that.

Unlike western hotel rooms that are little more than a bed and a bathroom, hostels in Yemen are more like mini-flats, with several bedrooms to accommodate large Yemeni families who often travel with one or several wives and all their kids. I watched my friends closing the deal from behind the black back windows of the car. When the deal was done, I slipped in our flat. No one noticed the unmarried foreigner who had just entered a hotel room with her fake brother and fake husband.

Qat

After 4pm the streets of Sana'a become empty. The contrast with the half an hour before is astonishing. At 3:30, the hectic crowds are moving fast, screaming, bumping into each other. It is the peak hour to buy qat and the qat markets boil with people and trade. Every day, the same scene repeats as a stream of men — students, workers, and beggars — flood the qat markets to buy the precious goods they will enjoy for the rest of the afternoon and into the late hours of the night.

Qat, scientifically known as catha edulis, is a small woody tree with fresh branches and bitter tasting leaves. Early every morning, qat farmers collect the fresh plant and distribute it for consumption. Not a single corner of the country is left without its portion and not a single man without his ration. Even if a man cannot afford to buy food for his family or provide education for his kids, he will find a way to pay for his daily dose of abstraction in the form of a plastic bag full of qat.

It is a very mild drug, milder than alcohol or weed, and only mildly addictive, but it is a key part of the daily routine and social atmosphere of Yemen. Weddings, social gatherings, meetings with friends... they all take place surrounded by qat. And there is a whole ritual for each step of the session.

First, as soon as you finish work, you go directly to the market. It is a special market. One street of each neighborhood used exclusively for selling qat. A row of stands fills the street and sellers sit behind each stand with their legs crossed, ready to distribute their product in small plastic bags.

You want to find the perfect leaves, so you check the stands till you find one that satisfies your taste and (hopefully) your budget. There are different kinds of qat and everyone has their favorite. The final effect is similar, but the texture of the leaves and the experience that comes with it varies. Thus, you can find qat for 250 Yemeni rial (about one US dollar) to 5,000, or even 10,000 rial if it has no pesticides. Qat is scarcer in winter, and thus the price goes up. If we take into account that most Yemeni live on less than two and a half dollars a day, to spend a dollar of that on drugs every day is a heavy charge.

Once you spot the plastic bag you want, you start negotiating the price with the seller. The best ones are always hidden so be clever and tell the creepy, gangster-looking seller to show you what he has tucked under his butt (yes, they literally sit on the good stuff). After going back and forth, you agree on the price, pay, and leave with your bag of qat hanging from your jambiya, the traditional dagger on your belt. (I am speaking like a man, because ladies, even though they chew on some occasions, are never supposed to go to qat market. It is men's territory.)

When you arrive home, get comfortable on a low couch with a pillow under one of your elbows, half lying on your side. Surround yourself with an empty ashtray, a pack of cigarettes, and a lot of water in small bottles. You should have 2 liters minimum, which you can combine with other sweet, fizzy drinks.

Now it is time. Maybe by yourself, but usually surrounded by friends, the magic starts.

Take small qat leaves out of the bag and chew them like a cow. Do not swallow them. Place the mashed leaves in one of your cheeks and store them there while you keep adding more and more. The leaves become a mushy mass that you keep in your mouth until the end of the session, which is a minimum of four hours, but can be up to eight if you do two consecutive chewing session, with the second session meant to cut the effect of the first one.

During the whole session, you sit there and chew and occasionally go to the toilet to evacuate the water you have been drinking in between pouring leaves into your cheek.

You also smoke from time to time at the beginning, until you are chain-smoking by the end. "Qat and cigarettes go so well together!" - any Yemeni would say. Old traditional music should be playing in the background, ideally, a man with a deep voice singing to the lover he lost. Finally, wrap your scarf around your head, a bit Tuareg style, to keep your head in place while your mind goes away.

Another important point to note is that the windows of the room must be completely closed. According to Yemeni belief, fresh air spoils the qat and airstreams can have bad effects. Thus, you have to keep your plastic bag closed while chewing to avoid air getting to it.

It is curious to see how at the beginning of these chewing sessions everyone is chatting to each other about this or that and slowly the room becomes silent as everyone focuses in on his own thoughts. This is exactly what qat is meant to do. It makes your body relaxed and lazy, but your mind aware of every sensation surrounding you and every thought running through your head. Imagine drinking 100 liters of black tea and 100 liters of lime blossom at a time and you will get an idea of the qat effect.

However, as with any drug, qat also has some side effects:

1 After chewing, it might be difficult to sleep. For that reason, from the moment you wake up the next day, you are just thinking of the moment you will be able to leave your workplace and go to chew again to counter this effect and feel awake again.

2 Men cannot sexually function, though with a birth rate of nine children per mother in Yemen (plus severe poverty), this might not be such a negative side effect.

3 Because of the heavy smoking that goes hand in hand with the chewing and the chemicals in the leaves, your lungs and your teeth become fucked up. And now, with the growing use of pesticides on qat farms, the negative impact on Yemeni health is increasing. Yemen now has one of the highest rates of mouth cancer in the world.

4 If you work in the afternoons - particularly shopkeepers - you will be so lazy while chewing that you will not want to move from the corner you are sitting in to serve your customers. And if customer service is usually bad, during chewing hours it's the worse. Some office owners encourage their employees to chew because qat also can help to focus your thoughts. And yes, it is true, you can spend eight hours focused on the computer screen in front of you, but the quality of the work also plummets so it ends up being more hours spent with lower quality results.

These effects are not a big deal if you chew once a week, but chewing every day can be quite destructive for your health and your pocket. And in Yemen most of the people not only chew every day of their life, but live primarily for the pleasure of chewing. It is, for them, a window to a world of dreams and an escape from daily reality.

Oh, but I forgot to mention how one ends a qat session. This is by far the most disgusting aspect of the ritual. You now must spit out all the leaves, which have congealed into a kind of muddy dough. The streets of Yemen are decorated with hundreds of millions of green spots, each of which marks the end of a qat session, and the beginning of a Yemeni chewers longing for the next.

CHAPTER 5

Our first morning in the coastal town of Hudeidah, I woke up hungry for food and adventure, but mostly craving my morning dose of caffeine. At a small restaurant next to the sea, we walked past the front entrance, which is exclusively for men, and made our way to the family entrance. We were led to a small room behind a red and pink curtain. The light had a roseate tone from the pink tapestry.

The family section is the place where men bring their wives and kids or where women go on the rare occasions that a group of ladies are out by themselves without their men. It is a handy arrangement, since it allows ladies to remove their *niqab* and eat much more comfortably without the presence of unwanted men. Curtains usually divide each table into a small private space so husbands cannot see anyone but their wives, and waiters usually pass the food from under the curtain and give it to the men without entering these private spaces. In smaller restaurants, like the one we were at, there was simply a curtain in the back of the restaurant dividing the last couple of tables from the rest.

Back in Sana'a, as a foreign lady I was sometimes allowed to sit in the male section, as long as I was accompanied. I didn't see the point in hiding behind a curtain when I didn't wear *niqab* to start with and every man in the restaurant had already seen my face. But since I was pretending to be local, we acted as such and went straight to the family section. The guys started debating their order from the *fasoulia* menu. There is nothing like starting the day with a typical Yemeni breakfast of beans, flat bread and sugary tea. *Fasoulia* bean dishes gives you energy for the whole day. You can choose wet beans, dry beans, beans with eggs, or beans with cheese. But I was too tired to care which bean dish we ate.

I had not fed my coffee addiction yet that morning and had despaired when I couldn't even find its proxy bun, a drink of brewed coffee casks. I sat gazing blankly at the pinky curtain. Until the food was placed in front of me on the table.

"I will bring you to a very special place today," Mr. Local said with his usual enthusiasm, taking a big bite of soupy beans.

First, I need some real coffee, I thought.

"My father used to take us there when we were kids with all my sisters," he continued.

Espresso would be great.

"I'm sure you will love it," he grinned.

Double espresso, would be even better. "Sounds great," I said, taking a gulp of sweet, creamy tea.

With OneRepublic blasting at full volume, we hit the road and drove down South to the beach. A bunch of men were swimming in their underwear where the long sandy beach began, so we drove a little bit further until we started to see families dispersed along the beach for some privacy. One here, another one over there, another a bit further, until finally we found our spot on an abandoned patch of beach. The guys removed their clothes and I removed my *niqab* and we walked directly to the sea.

I could see some other black spots far away jumping in the waves, so I decided to follow their *abbaya*-clad leads. It was my first time swimming with my clothes and *abbaya* on. It felt strange, the *abbaya* floated around me like an airbag. I was having a lot of fun experimenting with it, like a new attraction in a water park. It was so good to feel the salty water and the sun after such a long time. The last time I had a swim was at Pierre & Friends in Batroun (oh, lovely Lebanon) almost two years earlier. I'd grown up on the sea, and being in the water was reinvigorating.

When I finally emerged on the beach, the sun was strong, so I put some sunscreen on my nose and cheeks, the only exposed patches of skin that remained. We wrote our names in the sand, drawing big letters with our toes and taking pictures of our masterpieces. Once we were dry, we piled back in the car and headed to another beach farther north to watch the sunset, but not before a pit stop to buy some qat (Yemeni and their vice!). We got out of the car and followed a path through a small forest, emerging onto a superb little bay. The sun was big and red and we sat and watched it slowly going down till the last lines melted with the sea and painted the sky copper. I wanted to hug Mr. Local. Instead, I glanced at his friend and accepted his offering of qat. I chewed the leaves and let my mind drift away with the lapping waves.

When the sky was dark and mashed green paste filled our cheeks, we headed back to town and sat in one of the cafes by the shore. Nice company, shisha, and qat in front of the sea, what else does one need? The tea calmed the effect of the qat. I could feel new energy and strength in my body, but my mind was calm and relaxed. I wanted to always remember our pleasant day by the sea, so I replayed it over and over in my mind that night until I fell asleep.

We woke up late the next day and had a quick lunch in a fish restaurant before heading back towards Sana'a. We listened to a mix of Indian, Yemeni and Western hits, and after picking up our friend in his village, we had an easy drive through the army and tribal checkpoints. As soon as

I was back home in my small flat in the old neighborhood of that ancient city, the seaside escape began to feel as unreal as a dream. I looked at the pictures we'd taken. My crooked eye-mask. Mr. Local smiling. The expansive ocean. I didn't regret a single moment.

THE
CLUB
In Yemen

In our early days in Yemen, Bilma and I had desperately looked for a club. Coming from Beirut, with its amazing night life, I still had the urge to party. Bilma and I had been scouring online forums and Facebook, and calling hotels until one day we heard about an old club, long closed, which had reopened with a new name. It was called Club Istanbul.

It seemed that only foreigners were allowed to enter because it was inside a closed security compound where only expats could live. Despite our efforts to get more information about Club Istanbul's existence and location, for weeks we couldn't figure out anything else about it. We were pretty new in Yemen and our sources of information were limited. Asrat, our Ethiopian neighbor, was practiced in the art of Yemeni fishy affairs, so as soon as we updated him on the club's existence, he went on the hunt and didn't stop until he had the exact location and schedule.

So, there we were, the three of us, overly excited for our first clubbing night in Sana'a. The dress code was an important issue. Bilma and I had never been to a club in such a traditional country, and thus, we adopted a multi-layer approach.

Layer 1: *A disco sleeveless shirt.*
Layer 2: *A normal t-shirt.*
Layer 3: *A long-sleeved tunic.*
Layer 4: *Everything covered with our Batman cape and scarf.*

After putting on our make-up and a few drops of perfume, we were ready to go. Asrat needed an extra 20 minutes to decide what to wear. We left the house an entourage of onions with all our layers.

After some price negotiation, we took a taxi to the compound where six big soldiers stopped us at the gate. They checked our passports and let us go inside. It was the first and last time we made it in with so little drama. I'll call it beginner's luck. After that, getting through the gate was a weekly nightmare of bribes, begging, and negotiation.

Not knowing what to expect, we entered a dark restaurant and found it was empty. No one was there. Not a single person. We waved at a waiter. "Girls for free," he said, charging Asrat a not-so-small lump sum before showing us to the stairs that lead to the basement.

I pushed the door at the end of the stairs with enthusiasm and an explosion of disco lights and music appeared on the other side. I was so happy to be in a club that I didn't notice how small and creepy it was until halfway through the night.

The ventilation was bad, with no windows or fans, so the temperature inside was almost unbearable. The crowd also left a lot to be desired. The scene was composed of a few drunken old businessmen, probably contractors for construction and oil companies and a group of "working ladies" who kept them company. The girls danced and talked and cheered up the party. The bottom layer of our onion suits turned out to be modest compared to the minidresses worn inside the club.

That night Bilma, Asrat and I enjoyed music as if it was the first time we'd ever been clubbing in our lives. Fun does not come to you, you create your own fun, and our basement party was the first of many nights of dancing and laughs as we became unofficial VIP members of Yemen's awkward little club scene. All who entered were united by a desire to escape Yemen's restrictions and frustrations. For a very long time, that club was my drama-free zone. All the way up until the moment it wasn't.

CHAPTER 6

After our trip to Hudeidah, it seemed that Mr. Local's only concern was my happiness in Yemen. His soul was open and fearless. He was tender and enthusiastic, maybe because he had never been burned by previous experiences with love. We had to hide our relationship from everyone, even his best friends. I knew Bilma could sense something was going on and I was grateful that she respected our no-ask, wait-to-tell policy.

Even though we were surrounded by other people, we managed to steal a few private moments – holding hands in the backseat of the car, sharing inside jokes only we could understand – tiny little things that filled our hearts with happiness. Increasingly, Mr. Local managed to find ways to come to my flat alone or to stay longer when dropping me off. It felt like I was in a Yemeni Romeo and Juliet romance, hiding a forbidden love that we both knew would come to a tragic non-Hollywood end.

In the span of four months, Mr. Local, his two friends from the Hudeidah trip, and I, met for everything and anything Sana'a had to offer. We went out to drink tea or for a dinner of eggs and beans. We gathered on my terrace for fresh juice and drove in the mountains. There was a road that led to an amazing viewpoint from which I could see all of Sana'a. We would park there and wait for the shisha man to come. He would set up a plastic chair outside the car and place the shisha on it, passing the long pipe through the window. I loved it, though I found it disturbing to watch the eight-year old boy whose job it was to puff on the shisha pipes to get them started.

The guys called one afternoon to say they were on the way to pick me up. They wanted to take me to my favorite teashop for a glass of what is essentially sugar with a few drops of milk tea. We pulled up to the destroyed street corner where an old man ran a little tea shop. It was just him, a gas tank, and a couple of broken metal benches outside. The owner was very thin, with a long, unkempt white beard, and he was always surrounded by cats. He would get angry whenever the youngsters bothered the cats. Over the months, I had learned that the old man liked new bills. If I paid him with coins or old bills, he was fine, but when we handed him a new bill, allowing him to give the change back in ugly dirty ones, it made him really happy.

When I was a kid, I had loved my ugliest toys simply because they were so ugly that they were beautiful. This place was like that, a charmingly ugly place with a charmingly grumpy old man serving the best milk tea in the old city, or maybe in the whole of Sana'a. We sipped our cups of sugary tea and conversation turned to how this shabby place had much better tea than the shops in the malls in the rich neighborhoods of the city. I had seen Mr. Local in one of these malls a few days before when I was at a coffee shop drinking a truly terrible cappuccino. As I spoke, I could feel Mr. Local becoming more and more uncomfortable, but I continued. I didn't see the danger in speaking about cappuccinos and milk tea.

"The cappuccino was so bad, I don't know I could even call it coffee," I said.

"Wait, but who were you there with?" Mr. Local's talkative friend interrupted me to ask.

Panic washed over Mr. Local's face and he muttered a sentence in Arabic I couldn't understand.

"I was there with my two good friends from the Balkans, it was good luck we spotted each other," I added, confused at Mr. Local's reaction. I thought back to the exchange. He had met my Balkan friends before at a dinner in my house, so I thought nothing of it when they exchanged the typical pleasantries before he left to continue with his shopping. He had mainly addressed the two men, and had barely looked at me, but I hadn't seen anything strange about that since we were in a public place, and in Yemen, him talking directly to me, a woman, would have been the weird thing. I wondered why he was acting shy about it now.

"Oh, you were with your future brother-in-law?" Mr. Talkative blurted out. "What were you shopping for?"

A wave of jealousy swallowed me whole. He had been at the mall to buy his fiancée a small gift, a standard practice in Yemen to show the goodwill of the future husband to the girl and her family while couples are engaged.

"Nothing special," Mr. Local said, his cheeks becoming red.

"C'mon tell us, and we will tell you if it was a good choice of present or not," he continued. "We have a female insider here, so it is like having an expert. Did you get silver earrings?"

I sat pretending it had nothing to do with me and that I was neither interested in the subject nor annoyed by knowing more about it.

"Someone will have a nice time soon, marriage life," Mr. Talkative laughed, he seemed to be enjoying seeing his friend suffering from the awkward situation he was creating. "Cute little Mr. Locals all around..."

"Sorry guys, I have to go, but please you stay, I'll walk back home," I said, standing up. I had reached my limit. My poker face was wearing thin and I needed fresh air to collect my thoughts. To reach my home, I only had to cross one bridge and walk a couple of short streets, and after much protest about me walking home without an escort, they begrudgingly agreed.

Mr. Local was sensitive, and I knew he was probably burning with embarrassment after the awkward exchange. I didn't want him to worry, and I didn't want to hear an explanation, so I sent him a text as I walked. *Hey! I left the tea shop because I was tired, nothing to do with that conversation. Have a good night.* It was true, or I wanted to believe it was true. They were speaking of an engagement I already knew about, nothing new, so why should I be upset?

My phone chimed and I looked down at his reply. *Oh! You understand me so well, sending me this message... I was so preoccupied until I got it! Also, that day in the mall when you covered everything up so well and pretended we barely know each other? You behaved so perfectly! You ARE so perfect.*

I burst into tears. Did I behave perfectly? It was perfect for what? If I needed to hide something, it must be because it is not a good thing. Not only was I terrible for what I was doing, I was double terrible for knowing how to hide it. And he was praising me for it? With one message, the spell was broken.

Weddings
IN
YEMEN

It's wedding season in Yemen and you are invited to the wedding of the cousin of the friend of your colleague (yes, this happens). It is a big event and bringing some foreigners to a wedding adds a bit of glamour and gossip to the party. But, wait a minute...in Yemen wedding time means double weddings, because every wedding is, in fact, two weddings: the lady's party and the man's party.

But don't worry, that does not mean you will need to pay for two wedding gifts. No. It is not an economic matter, it is simply that women will go to the ladies' party and men will go to the men's. (In the case that you don't want to define your gender, Yemen is not a good place for you to live in general.)

So, it all starts this way. One day you receive a very fancy envelope with an overly cheesy wedding card inside announcing the day and place of the wedding. The name of the bride is not written on it, only the family name, in case any of your male relatives spy the card and discover the name of his friend's daughter (the scandal!).

On the day in question, you put on a dress and one hundred kilos of make-up, followed by all the gold you can possibly find in your house. Silver doesn't count, any other metal doesn't count, but if you have any golden cutlery put it on your neck and in your hair, because girl, gold is gold in Yemen. Finish things off by dousing one hundred and five liters of strong perfume all over your body, dress, shoes, and bag, and then cover yourself from head to toe with your black cape before heading outdoors.

A male relative or taxi will drive you to the wedding hall. Weddings usually start in the afternoon, around four or five o'clock at the latest, and they last till eight or nine in the evening. It wouldn't be proper for a female to stay outside past these late hours. So, you arrive at the wedding hall wearing your Cinderella dress and your Batman cape.

I always try to arrive as late as possible, since as you will soon learn, fun is not the right word to describe the occasion.

Two ladies at the entrance register your bag and make sure you don't enter with any camera or phone with a camera, which is perfect for me, because I have a very old phone with no color on the screen. Inside you are not allowed to take pictures, because all the girls go uncovered and you could show the pictures to your male relatives or friends (the shame!).

You enter the hall, which is a big room decorated with plastic flowers made in China and a long catwalk in the middle with a throne at the end. Music plays from a CD, likely a mix of the latest Egyptian hits. Old and young ladies alike attend the wedding wearing the brightest dresses you've ever seen — bright blue, bright pink, bright blue dress with bright pink tights — coming together as a kind of mix and match anti-fashion. The more outlandish, the better. Another point is the bra. It doesn't matter if what you're wearing, white or beige, grandma bras can be seen from all the angles of the room as transparent straps and strapless bras have not arrived yet to Yemen. To finish the pale bra and bright dress look, add the famous layer of gold I spoke about. One necklace, then another one, and another one. Bracelets, pendants, earrings. Wear them all. And when I say all, I mean all. You don't leave any gold piece in the bottom of your drawer. All is All.

Upon arrival, remove your Batman cape and retouch your look. It is okay to bring your hairdryer or curling iron with you and some extra tons of make-up. Feel free to plug it in in front of the other hundred girls in the room and start doing your hair or nails in the middle of the wedding. About 99 other girls will be doing the same.

Once you have had enough of your beauty treatment, go and sit. If you are lucky, there will be some chairs around, if not, you can sit on the floor or on the traditional coaches at ground level. Old ladies are allowed to chew qat during the wedding and smoke the traditional shisha, a longer wooden version filled with really strong, unflavored tobacco. It will make you cough and feel dizzy after the first puff. If you are middle-aged, you can smoke shisha, but if you are young, you just sit and eat the sunflower seeds you brought from home. The bride is not yet there, so since you cannot gossip about her at the start of the event, you gossip about the guests. You gossip and gossip and gossip. Observe all the other ladies sitting there and become as envious as you can of their gold. Stare at them and give them bad looks because they have one more gold necklace than you do. Then, keep on waiting.

If you are unmarried, and therefore most likely under 18, lucky you, you are allowed to dance! You can dance with all the little daughters and sons of the other guests, because you cannot bring your husband to the wedding, but you are almost forced to bring all your offspring with you. And you can dance with the other unmarried female teenagers.

Weddings are the best opportunities for unmarried girls to find a husband. All the mums of unmarried guys will be there looking for potential candidates. So, if you are dancing, most likely some older ladies have spotted you and will come over to chitchat. They will ask you for your family name. When these ladies go back home that night, they will report to their sons and explain all the ladies they have checked out, with the hope that one of them will meet the criteria set by their sons. In case one of these girls does, and the boy wants to get married, a male relative (probably the uncle) will go to the girl's house and talk to the father of the girl and see if they would be interested in a potential marriage deal. This ensures that the next wedding season will be again full of weddings.

But back to our wedding. You are there, sitting, listening to the other girls gossiping and waiting. You wait and wait and wait, and when you think you cannot handle one more of those songs played on the old CD player *tada!* the bride enters the room. Slowly, very slowly, she walks towards the catwalk. The other girls are cheering, but she looks straight ahead towards the throne, which is waiting for her at the edge. Most of the time you cannot recognize the bride; even if the bride is your sister. Her body is covered in henna decorations, amazing patterns that cover all her body. Her face is covered in a white paste so thick you could dip your food in it. Her eyes are painted with thick black eyeliner and multicolor bright eye shadows. The girl, almost without breath, moves slowly all along the platform. One small step now, one after thirty seconds, and little by little approaches the throne. Girls are applauding and cheering. But under all that makeup, the bride has a look of terror on her face. I can always spot the nervousness and feel her fear. This is the sad part.

The bride has not interacted with males other than her father and brother in her lifetime, she does not know anything about relationships, not even how humans conceive. But she does know that she will soon be dropped into her husband's bed. The bed of a guy she has not chosen, met, or seen before. Even if she doesn't know what this means, her intuition tells her that what lies ahead is not a glittering pink world like that of the wedding hall. But girls in Yemen are brave, very brave, so the bride keeps on walking that catwalk, surrounded by plastic flowers and balloons.

At long last, she reaches the throne and the wedding is over. *Cheers!* This is it. Time for all the ladies to cover up again with their Batman cover and call their male guardians for a fast pickup so they can be back home next to their husbands before it gets too late.

I enjoyed the first couple of weddings I attended. It was curious for me to see them and observe how the ladies behaved. I saw some amazing make-up fashion. I also went to the smaller weddings of poorer families. They were much nicer, with only the sisters and cousins of the bride, her mum, and sisters and the mum of her future husband. The atmosphere was much less pretentious and more joyful. The ladies were simply dancing and enjoying their last minutes together as they were. That night, the bride would start a new life in a new house, with her new family. Once you marry, your family changes. You belong to your husband's family starting at that moment and for the rest of your life. If your husband is good, he will allow you to go and visit your mum and sisters frequently, but if he is not, you will see them maybe once or twice a year, for special occasions and festivities. Because of this, the small parties were nicer, but fear in the bride's eyes was as sad as always. That is why at some point, I started to decline wedding invitations.

I also had the chance to crash some men's weddings, but fewer, and only for a short five or ten minutes to watch what was going on. For the men, a wedding takes place in a big canvas tent on the street. All the men sit and chew qat while the groom sits in a special chair decorated with flowers. Every guest goes to congratulate the groom, take a picture with him, and then find a place to sit and chew. At the end of the chewing party, the men dance together, hand-in-hand, and shoot their guns in the air to celebrate.

Don't tell them, but sometimes ladies spy on them from the roofs of surrounding buildings, watching like visitors to a foreign land.

CHAPTER 7

The moment I reached home I started to feel extremely sick. I vomited non-stop and could feel the energy draining from my body. I was in very bad shape, lying on the couch when Bilma arrived an hour later. I had a high fever and she carried me to my bed to sleep. I passed the night in terrible condition and the next day I wasn't any better. I knew it was all the accumulated guilt from the previous month, eating me from inside.

Mr. Local did not know his fiancée and the fiancée didn't know him, but for me it was technically cheating, and this was a real moral problem for me. If I were a cold, rational person, I could have justified our relationship, but I was a nun-educated villager who couldn't lie. As I lay in bed, I could not stop thinking about what a vile, terrible person I was. I was feeling guilty, and guilt was one of the most terrible feelings one can have. The entire relationship was immoral and unacceptable. The nuns started in again: Complete. Unacceptable. Behavior.

Mr. Local kept calling me the next day, he had the feeling something wasn't right and called Bilma when I didn't answer. Two hours later, he and his talkative friend were at my house. In my sick state, I didn't want to be seen, I didn't want them to pity me and I couldn't bear to have Mr. Local see my pale face and matted hair. But I was too weak to protest. I was half asleep when I heard their voices in the living room. They brought yoghurt, raw garlic, and honey. For Yemeni people this is a miraculous remedy for any sort of stomach virus you might have, and Bilma promised she would give me the magic medicine later when I was awake. I was grateful for her lie, it was the last thing I wanted to eat, and they certainly would have sat and watched me eat it if she hadn't been there. She ushered them out and she came back a short while later to check on me.

For the next full week, I remained in bed. Mr. Local passed by every day, sometimes twice a day, to bring food for Bilma, and bread, yoghurt and rice for sick me. I refused to see him, but knowing that he would come every day, was a comfort and a torment. I knew I had to end the relationship, but at the same time I desperately wanted to hold on to the happiness he brought me. *Hi! I hope you can understand this MESS-age.* I typed. *Do you remember after tea when you wrote to me and told me how well I understand you?* I looked down at the screen, unsure if I would ever hit send. I wasn't a sentimental person, maybe I just needed to type out my feelings to clear my mind... *the message you sent me made me realize we have to stop. If I don't stop seeing you now, the guilt will find me later. I'm glad we met. I'm glad we spent good times together, I'm glad we shared crazy laughter together, I'm glad you showed me terrible Hollywood movies with happy endings. And I am sure we will always be good friends. So, let's enjoy the few weeks we have left only as that, just good friends.*

I deleted the message.

When he called, I still wasn't sure what I wanted to say or when I wanted to say it. "All is perfectly alright, fully recovered from the virus now" I said, and we hung up. Two hours later, he was knocking on my door. Even though I am very good at hiding my feelings, Mr. Local was even better at discovering them. He had been on the other side of Sana'a with no car, and spent the two hours in a crowded mini bus to reach my house. By the time he arrived, it was almost time for him to leave again so he could make it home in time for his family-imposed curfew. When I opened the door, he held me in a long embrace.

"What's wrong?" he asked with a preoccupied face.

I look funny when I try to speak about my feelings. I can't put coherent sentences together and my speech becomes clumsy. I just start sentences and cut them short after only a couple of words. This only happens when I speak about something deep that hurts me. It was in this stumbling, fumbling way that I tried to explain to Mr. Local everything that was in my head. He looked at me with a fixed, worried look in his big green eyes as he tried to absorb every single word I said. My eyes were wet. Only a few people had ever seen me cry. I like to say it is a once in a lifetime show. When I finished talking, he just stared at me.

"You are so beautiful, only good people feel guilty, bad ones don't even think about it," he said. I cried and laughed at the same time. "I can only like you more now, after knowing how you feel, I really lo..." and he cracked. Tears filled his big green eyes, rolling down his porcelain cheeks, and he at last opened up. "My family only allowed me to go to study in Malaysia on the condition to get engaged before I left. And I agreed to get married immediately after finishing my studies in exchange. I could not contradict my family – he sobbed. "I don't even know her! Can you believe? She is the younger sister of one of my friends from primary school. I vaguely remember her from when she was a kid in the girls' section of the school. I have not seen her since then, not even at the engagement, and I will not see her again until their wedding day." His voice sounded so sad as he explained the situation. He was a romantic by nature and getting married to someone he did not know was a painful idea. "My wedding day will mark the end of living life the way I always wanted to".

I'd thought a lot about the fate of the poor girls in Yemen who were married off to husbands chosen for them by their families. I had imagined the horror those girls must have felt in the early days of their marriages to men they did not know, and with whom they would spend the rest of their lives. I found the idea terrifying. I'd never thought about the men in quite the same way till that day.

We talked for hours. He missed his curfew. I felt closer to him than ever before. We had two weeks left before his departure, but I had to travel outside Sana'a for 10 days for work. Cruel life. That left us with only one more chance to see each other and say goodbye.

A HORNY
Nation

My Bosnian friend, a doctor who has been living in Yemen for the past 6 years, has reached a very interesting conclusion based on non-scientific research collected through daily life observations: Yemen is a horny nation and all the problems of Yemen derive from this fact.

The whole society is organized following a gender segregation criterion with a very simple golden rule: Avoid interaction with the other gender as much as possible if you want to (1) save your reputation, (2) save your family's reputation and (3) save your ass. This rule applies first and foremost to the public space. Schools for boys, schools for girls; one side of the bus for men, the other side for women; two-floor restaurants with two separate entrances, one only for men, the other one for families. In fact, the street is considered men's territory and therefore women avoid being outside as much as possible.

Is that covered-from-head-to-toe lady walking alone in the street? Either she is doing something bad, or she is horny and looking for mambo. These are the only two thoughts that pop up in the brain of Yemeni men. When ladies do go out, alone or accompanied, they avoid any interaction with men to the point of calling their male relatives to speak on their behalf to the taxi drivers or the sellers in the shops. Looking at a man directly in his eyes? Hell no! That would mean she is looking for mambo. Letting her voice be heard? Hell no! That would mean she is looking for mambo. Walking fast or moving the body? Mambo. Laughing in public? Mambo. Nail polish, colorful shoes or no socks? You guessed it, mambo.

This leads to a society where in the daily life of a man he does not speak, touch or see any women apart from his first line of female relatives: mother, sisters, daughters and wives. Thus, you have each Yemeni man having seen no more than 10 uncovered women (and I am not exaggerating) in his lifetime.

And what do all these mambo misconceptions and minimum gender interactions lead to? Zero knowledge of the other sex, which makes things really complicated, particularly when it comes to...sex.

"Men are in the streets and cannot see any women, only walking blankets passing by. Their imagination thinks that these walking blankets are Sharon Stones with dirty minds looking for mambo, but a mambo they cannot even try to get because it is socially unacceptable to approach any women," my doctor friend starts explaining his theory. "They arrive home horny with these thoughts and they see their wives who were married to guys they didn't know before and who know nothing about sex (this is a big taboo subject in Yemeni society). They don't like each other, and they have bad sex, so men do not release their stress. Since they are stressed, they go and chew qat to calm down but after having qat they cannot function sexually so they get even more stressed and frustrated. So, they go out for tea and see covered Sharon Stones passing by, which make them even hornier." A real catch 22, as he explained, from a very male-oriented perspective, I must say.

And you may wonder, what about expatriates living there? Due to the harsh environment and the security situation, there are almost no female expats working in the country. The ratio is 1 female expat to 80 males. Everyone knows what happens when excess demand is coupled with shortage of supply: in the eyes of men, all expat women start to look like Pamela Anderson in her red bikini. It might sound cynical to apply laws of microeconomics to love affairs, but in Yemen, supply and demand are unequal and this has an unbelievable effect on the attention expat women get. As my friend Bilma used to put it, if you are a female expat in Yemen, it does not really matter if you are beautiful, young and charming, or an ugly and mean, either way you will live surrounded by thirsty wolves giving you all their attention, whether you want it or not.

CHAPTER 8

I came back from my assignment outside the capital in the late afternoon. I needed a couple of hours to reach my house and get ready. I was in terrible condition after working for ten days in the middle of nowhere. Mr. Local called to ask if I had any problems at the airport or with the taxi and he agreed to come over around 9 p.m.

When he arrived he looked happy. That evening, he had no curfew so he could stay as long as we wanted. He brought me my favorite strawberry juice and a *ruti* white cheese sandwich. "I know you forget to eat when you are in the field, all the way until you starve," he said as he handed the *ruti* to me.

I savored the small details, the way he took care of me in a way I hadn't been cared for since I was a child. We talked for a long time. We talked about his trip back to Malaysia to finish his studies, we talked about our lives and our futures, we talked about how precious our time together had been. It was getting later and later, but we were in no hurry, we wanted to enjoy every single minute we had left together. We looked at pictures from our first trip to Hudeidah by the sea, laughing as we recounted every single detail.

At some point we became melancholic. It was unavoidable. We held each other for a long while.

I didn't want to cry. "I wish you all the best in your life, I really wish that," I said.

He took a little bag from his pocket and pulled out a silver necklace set with turquoise stones. He placed it carefully around my neck. He was crying as we hugged one last time.

The moment he closed the door behind him, I started crying, too. I kissed the turquoise around my neck and whispered, "Goodbye."

Adventure 2
The Stubborn Engineer

CHAPTER 9

The Stubborn Engineer I found in Yemen, or to be more precise, the one who found me, was a control freak with a macho attitude. But let me start at the beginning; the day Bilma and I went clubbing at Metropolis. After Club Istanbul was closed down after a big fight broke out inside, Metropolis became the only available alternative. It was a bigger, fresher disco in the basement of a posh hotel. It was managed by the same manager, staffed with the same DJ, and attended by the same crowd. New place, new name, same old thing. We were there with a pair of Lebanese brothers we had met a week earlier. The boys seemed content to just sit drinking at the table. Bilma and I were in the mood to shake our bodies, so we headed to the dance floor without them. The place was surprisingly full, and though we were no match for the group of *Khaliji* ladies who moved their heads and swung their hair dancing expertly in their unique Gulf-style, we joined them anyways. I swayed with my signature Latino moves and let the music take me away.

Bilma had traded her nerdy office look of tight bun and black-rimmed glasses for a free and splendorous wavy mane, soft make-up, and a tight party dress. A young man approached her. The guy looked pretty normal, surprisingly normal for Yemen, and cute. We learned he was a Turkish architect who had recently arrived. I smoothly slipped off the dance floor, heading back to the table where I could still keep an eye on them. I took a sip of my drink and turned to talk to our Lebanese friends. Then I saw movement out of the corner of my eye. A man cut straight across the dance floor, charging towards Bilma and her new boy like a bullet. I stood up, worried a fight was about to start. The man embraced the Turkish architect and I breathed a sigh of relief. The three chatted for a while, then the bullet left the new couple to continue dancing.

As the night wound down, I joined Bilma and her new friend for the last dance of the evening. By the time I reached them, the human bullet had reappeared. The four of us danced until the music cut off and the lights went up.

"This guy is really after you," Bilma whispered and nodded towards the bullet. "He says he knows you." I looked at him again, taking in the details of his face. It did look familiar, but I couldn't figure out from where. "He told me he's been crazy about you since last year and he wanted me to give him your phone number, but I told him to fuck off and ask for it himself."

I grinned at her, my lovely Bilma. After the Mr. Local soap opera, my strike was back on and my resolve was stronger than ever. If this man, or any man, wanted my number, he had to dare to come and ask for it himself. Then I would enjoy the pleasure of kindly declining.

When the bullet man approached me, I tried to avoid him using moves worthy of the best tango. Each of his steps forward were met with two of mine back, until I found myself trapped between him and the bar. "I have seen you before in Club Istanbul," he said, the smell of whiskey coming off his breath. "I have seen you many times there. You drive me crazy, but I never had the chance to meet you."

I rolled my eyes. *Couldn't he drink gin? At least the smell would be better!* I turned to glare at him and realized that I did recognize his face from my very early days at Club Istanbul. He had caught my attention with his white shirt with two opened buttons, Mediterranean style, a perfectly trimmed lumberjack beard, and a sharp look in his black eyes. Back then, he always seemed to be talking to the owner, Mahmoud. I remembered thinking that he fancied himself the second boss of that mafia place. Yes, he had definitely caught my eye with his sexy beard, but I never bothered to ask Mahmoud or anyone else about him. Then one day, he just disappeared.

"No, sorry. It is the first time I'm seeing you," I proudly replied. "But nice to meet you, anyways." I stepped around him, took Bilma by the arm, and we left.

PARIS, LONDON, MILAN?

Fashion in Yemen!

In Yemen, ladies cover from head to toe. The old ladies wear the traditional outfit, a big multicolor piece of fabric. They wrap it around their tiny, bony bodies and head, while holding the edge by biting it. In every region of Yemen, the textile has a different pattern. In the capital, it is decorated with blue, yellow and red flowers. In the northeast, you'll see orange, red and black. Down south, lines of orange, gold, red and black are woven in. The textiles are diverse, colorful, and beautiful to look at. However, only the older ladies, mostly the ones who live in villages, wear this traditional outfit.

The new generation have copy and pasted the fashion from richer neighboring countries, wearing typical, long black robes that are 100% black. Which is the same color they use to cover hair and face, thus rendering the streets of Yemen a sea of black spots.

This new fashion, imported only a generation ago, is now found in every corner of the country. It is a three-piece outfit worthy of cinema. Piece number one is The Batman Cape, which covers from shoulders to toes. Piece number two is The Ninja Scarf, which is worn around the forehead and hair. Piece number three is The Zorro Eye Mask, which covers the entire face except for a tiny little band at the eye level. This exposed band of skin will either be covered with approximately one ton of make-up (if you are from Yemen) or sunblock cream (if you are foreigner and get sunburned as fast as I do).

There is also a third possibility for this little strip of skin. Toxic whitening cream. All ladies in Yemen seem to want their skin to be as white as possible. I am repeatedly asked by my beloved female colleagues about which skin cream brand I use, as they are of the opinion that it is really working well for me. They always get angry when I tell that I don't use skin whitening cream, only sunblock. My skin is olive color and it is as nice as any other skin tone, but burns very fast. Sadly, they don't believe me, and insist that I am hiding my most sacred beauty secret from them.

Before arriving in Yemen, I loved the color black. It's elegant, it's slimming, and it's chic...but hell! Two years in black and you will feel the depressing effects on your mood. Call me old-fashioned, but I have become a big fan of the traditional colorful style. I beg of the new generations of Yemen, bring it back amid cheers of *long live color!*

Shoes are another important point. They need to be ugly. They should not have a heel and you need to wear socks with them if they are open-toed. Ladies, your pinkie toe is so sexy, you could create an accident if a man sees it. I once made the mistake of walking in the streets with sandals and no socks. To make matters worse, my toenails were painted cherry red. I attracted a lot of unwanted attention that day. I still wear sandals without socks (it is my little act of rebellion), but only if my toenails aren't painted. A trick I learned from my Yemeni girlfriends is to always have an extra pair of clean socks in my bag, just in case I randomly decide to go to the salon and get a pedicure in the brightest color I can find. Not a bad idea to also have a pair of spare gloves as well, just in case there is an offer for mani-pedi.

What about men's fashion? It offers a wider range of choices than the standard black of women's attire. Men can dress in the traditional way or in a more western style. The traditional outfits are a long immaculate white *thoube* or a kind of skirt called *mawaz* wrap around their legs that comes to just above the knee. This reveals far too many unsexy legs, so when crossing a crowded street, you're apt to see more male flesh than you'd prefer. The patterns on this sort of skirt are amazing: colorful designs on silky fabric. The skirt stays in place thanks to a big embroidered belt, usually golden and green, though I have sometimes seen ones made out of red, blue and tiny yellow beads in the towns near the sea. The belt is also used to hold the *jambiya* in place. The *jambiya*, a half-moon shaped dagger is the most important item in the wardrobe of any Yemeni man. The handle is made out of bone and men usually inherit them, passing them down from generation to generation. To buy a good one is expensive. Unaffordable to most.

To threaten someone with a dagger is considered really offense and demands a determined reaction on the spot. However, they are typically more decorative, than anything else. Most of the time, the dagger serves as a hook on which to hang plastic bags after some light shopping.

To create a unique look, most men turn to the styling of their scarf, which is also made of nice textiles with rich colors and intricate designs. Don't be fooled. A scarf is not simply a scarf. It needs to be strategically placed around the neck or the head in creative ways to achieve the man's signature look.

And no outfit would be complete without a gun. Carrying arms in Yemen is standard practice and every man must have one, although the choice to carry it all the time or just on special occasions, like weddings and tribal gatherings, is up to the individual. You might be surprised to know that Yemeni men match their weapons with their attire. AK-47s are for classic occasions. Small guns, James Bond-style, offer a more urban look. Forgoing the gun in favor of a dagger is a retro choice. Electroshock weapons are the ultimate choice for ladies, perfect for carrying in a medium-size bag (they may not be very girlish, but they are highly effective).

Although bullet prices have hit rock bottom these days, inflation has ravaged Yemen's economy, which means one's gun has to last for years, and one must take good care of it. What better way to protect this vital piece of equipment than by wrapping scotch tape around the handle? When I asked about the function of the tape, I was told: *You wouldn't want an ugly scratch on the wood of Kalashnikov. It will ruin the look!*

CHAPTER 10

To my surprise, Bilma gave her telephone number to the architect. This had never happened before and I hoped that Mr. Architect knew how lucky he was to get my bestie's phone number. It only took him a day to invite us for coffee. Sleepy after the night out and our weekly weekend duty of house cleaning, we headed to a café on Hadda road. When we arrived, Mr. Architect and The Bullet were there waiting at a table outside. Bilma and I were bloody late, as usual, and they looked annoyed. On second glance, The Bullet looked more nervous than annoyed as he compulsively smoked cigarette after cigarette.

Bilma and Mr. Architect jumped right into a fluid conversation and I tried to engage with the nervous chimney. "How do you guys know each other?" I asked. "Are you friends or do you work together?"

"Yes," he said.

"So, you are also an architect?"

"Of course not," he snapped. "I am an engineer."

"Oh, okay. It must be nice to see your projects developing..."

"What do you know about our projects?" he cut in mid-sentence.

I took a breath, trying not to get angry. Perhaps there was a language barrier and he was nervous. I glanced at Bilma. She looked so happy. I needed to keep the conversation up for her sake. "Nothing, that's why I am asking..."

"True, you don't know anything," he replied rudely.

It was becoming harder to hide my exasperation. "You tell me, then," I brusquely said. "What are you working on now?"

"Work, work, work," he punctuated his words with stabs of his cigarette in the ashtray. "Everyday, 10 hours, that's it."

"Where do you live?" I asked, making one last attempt at a conversation.

"As if you didn't know," he snorted. "In Expat House, as all of us do."

I looked straight at him for a minute before turning my attention to my phone. He had managed to rile me. I never accepted rude comments from men I knew well, let alone from a random guy I'd just met. I decided to enjoy my coffee and ignore him.

Even in silence he managed to irritate me. Whenever I glanced up, I caught him staring at a fixed point on my forehead, a little bit above my eyes, just where my hairline started. I ran my hand over my hair, wondering if something was on my face, or if my hijab had shifted back. The second time, I looked up and caught him staring, I openly glared at him.

"You don't know anything about me, but I do know a lot about you," he said, suddenly.

I raised one eyebrow while my eyes went back to my phone screen.

"You and your roommate Bilma should stop chewing qat with all those journo friends of yours in Beyt Salim, they are of no good."

I glanced up at him, trying to hide my surprise. How could he know that? Bilma and I occasionally chewed with a few French journalists who lived in our quarter in old Sana'a, but they were not party people and had no interest in the crowd hanging out in Expat House. They were from two completely different expat worlds in the same city, and as far as I knew, the only connection between the two were Bilma and I.

"Sounds like now you are talking about things you don't know," I said, smiling an icy smile.

"I know," he said. "My information is always reliable."

I was relieved when the waiter came with the bill. I had made up my mind, no matter what, I would never see the entirely rude engineer again. Bilma and I smiled at them and politely said goodbye, before jumping in a minibus headed to Old Sana'a.

"How did it go? Did you get along?" asked Bilma as the bus pulled away.

"Two fishes in a fishbowl would have more to say to one another," I said. "But your guy looks cute, and you seemed to enjoy his company, so you should see him again."

"Maybe," Bilma said. "And they live in Expat House."

"Yes, with a bunch of other thirsty, Turkish wolves."

"Yeah, but still, if we go to visit, we'll finally get a chance to see the compound in the daytime," she shrugged.

"Don't count me in," I said. "As interesting as that place would be for an anthropologist, I don't plan to see that stubborn Engineer again."

The notorious Expat House was located in the same compound that had housed the now defunct Club Istanbul. The complex was protected by Yemen's army and only foreigners were allowed to enter. The very strict access meant everyone was required to show their passports at the entrance. After 10 p.m., access was almost solely dependent on the mood of the guard. If he was chewing good qat or received a good bribe, entry would be no problem. If he was in a bad mood that night, no one would get inside, including those who lived there.

The housing area consisted of several buildings, which were home to the employees of a big foreign construction company and its subcontractors, as well as the stewardesses working for the crappy airlines that connected Yemen with the outside world. It also hosted the very small community of Yemeni Jews still living in the country.

The buildings were separated by gender. A secured complex with 400 macho Turks and maybe 50 Filipina beauty queen wannabes was a recipe for drama. Continuous rumors and tattles fed the bored minds of its inhabitants, rival groups emerged, each with a different Turkish sachem wanting to be the boss of the place. It was like an ongoing episode of Big Brother, or Big Brothel, with its inhabitants changing partners as often as they changed their underwear. I was curious about the place, but no amount of curiosity would be enough to make me want to spend another minute with the Engineer again.

CHAPTER 11

"I got some gossips for you!" Bilma sang as she burst into our apartment and jumped directly on the couch in our *majlis* where I sat typing. It seemed that her third consecutive Friday coffee date with Mr. Architect had gone well. "Okay, tell me," I laughed, closing my computer.

"Well, it sounds like Mr. Engineer is the de facto boss of Expat House."

"Really?" I said, raising an eyebrow.

"Do you remember you told me you had seen him hanging out with Mahmoud, the owner of Club Istanbul? Well, apparently, they were actually in competition. They got into a fist fight at the club almost a year ago, something about a woman they were both interested in, and Mahmoud strategically banned him from the club. I think that evening we had been there before the fight broke out." Her eyes sparkled as she told the story.

"That explains his disappearance," I said, standing and moving towards the kitchen. "Did you have fun, you little devil?"

"Yes. Big steps. Mr. Architect has invited me for brunch at his home in Expat House next week."

"Ah," I said, focusing on making coffee and silently praying she would not ask me to join.

"Please, please, please come with me," she begged. " I don't want to go there alone."

I sighed. She already knew the answer. She knew I wouldn't send her into the lion's den on her own.

And so, we went. The Stubborn Engineer spent hours cooking for us that Friday. The brunch was delicious. A selection of Kisir salad, with bulgur, tomes, mint and pomegranate molasses; carrot, apple, walnut salad in yoghurt dressing; oven-baked fish on a bed of eggplant, zucchini, and homemade mashed potatoes; and a banquet of marinated meat barbequed to-order on the terrace. It was a pleasure for the senses, and I ate until my stomach felt like it was about to explode. Even Bilma's seemingly unlimited appetite was satisfied. I had never met anyone who enjoyed food the way Bilma did. Her daily routine revolved around mealtimes and between meals she thought only of what she would eat next. Whenever I ate with her, I somehow ended up eating twice what I normally would, simply because watching her utter joy at eating for the pleasure of it made me want to savor with the same abandon.

In addition to eating ourselves sick, we played the part of the good guests by sipping Turkish raki, an anise-flavored drink, though not as fast as the boys drunk it.

"Why do people think the way to a man's heart is through his stomach?" she leaned over and whispered. "Why do they think it only applies to men? Gastrosexuals are always welcome!"

I laughed and took a bite of sweet melon with white cheese. "I would kill for some coffee," I said quietly.

"I will teach you how to make Turkish coffee," Mr. Engineer said, standing up. He wobbled and I could tell the raki was already having its effect.

"Why don't you make it for us, if you are so good at it?" I asked, really not wanting to go anywhere with him, even into the kitchen.

"Come," he insisted stubbornly.

Since I adore coffee as much as Bilma adored food, I relented and followed him into the kitchen.

"I have fought such a long time for you," he said, as the pot was starting to boil.

Pardon? I thought. You have only known me for a couple weeks... I stayed quiet, watching as he poured two spoons of coffee into the pot.

"The other people in Club Istanbul were only speaking BS about you to make me mad".

"Ein...?" I started to say, wondering who and what he was talking about. But I stopped, reminding myself that I didn't care about the rumors circulating inside the closed little world of Expat House. All I cared about was having a good cup of coffee.

"They were courting you, but I told them since the beginning that you are my girl," he said, stirring my poor coffee as if it was a washing machine. If I had known how long a process it was to make Turkish coffee, I might have considered giving up my caffeine addiction.

He opened a cupboard and wobbled as he took out an old ugly cup, trying to push a forgotten satellite radio deep inside of the cupboard and out of the way. "You are the reason for all my fights in Club Istanbul. After my fight with Mahmoud, I couldn't enter there anymore, but I knew I would find you again."

I watched in horror as the coffee boiled, furious that after putting up with his crazy stories, I would have to drink burned coffee as well.

ALL
ABOUT
Respect

One day, about three months after I'd arrived in Yemen, I was walking down the street heading to my office when I saw four men in a circle surrounding what I thought was a dead body. When I got closer, I saw that it was a woman, and the men looked concerned.

It was a very warm day and she had collapsed, probably due to sunstroke, and she was still face-down and unconscious in the same place where she had landed. The men wanted to flip her over so she was facing up and could breathe more easily, but there was a problem. To touch her would tarnish her honor. This left them with only one option, to scream and panic, which is what they began to do.

Even though her face was covered, I could see that she was an old lady. I tried to roll her over, but she was so heavy I could barely move her. The three men looked down at me, exasperated and unable to help either of us. After a few failed attempts, finally I managed to lift her up. I motioned for the men to step back, then I lifted the mask covering her face. Her eyes fluttered and opened, and I handed her a bottle of water offered by one of the men. I used another bottle to clean the blood from a wound she had next to her eye.

Gradually she pulled around and, leaning on me, she managed to sit up in a white plastic chair one of the men had brought from his food shop. After a while, an old man, presumably her husband, came to fetch her. Leaning on each other, they teetered away down a back alley. I imagined one of the men had recognized who she was and had gone to tell her family.

As I continued on towards the office, my annoyance grew. The men had genuinely wanted to help the poor old woman, but touching her to put her face up or seeing her face after I lifted her mask would have been detrimental to her reputation. They respected her too much to violate her modesty, and it seemed that preserving her honor was a higher priority than potentially saving her life. I wondered which she valued more. I wondered if it would have mattered.

CHAPTER 12

Bilma was right, Gastrosexuals do get extra points. Whether a genius ploy or dumb luck, the Engineer seemed to have discovered that Bilma's weak spot was food, and my weak spot was Bilma. Mr. Architect lacked any skills in the kitchen, so the Engineer kept cooking and Bilma kept asking me to go along with her. I became an unwilling part of the foursome.

Publicly, the Stubborn Engineer had convinced all his friends, and most of his enemies, that I was his de facto girlfriend. They had all stopped talking to me, whether they saw me in a café or dancing at the club. I wasn't sure if the Engineer directly threatened them, or if the potential for drama was simply not worth it. Either way, I was still on strike, so his efforts worked in my favor. Privately, he was frustrated we were not dating. And I was enjoying his frustration as a payback for how annoying he was.

He tried very hard. Calls, texts, invites. The more I rejected him, the harder he tried. Every evening we would have the same phone conversation.

"Babe?" he'd say.

"Hi, how are you today?" I'd chirp. "And I am not your babe."

"Ok."

"How was work?"

"Tiring... a lot of work."

"Again? Poor you."

(silence)

"And nothing new?"

"No."

(Silence. This would be the moment I started not paying attention to the conversation.)

"Where are you?"

"In a Jacuzzi with five boys."

"Ahnn... are you home, right?"

"Yes."

"Ok."

(silence)

"I need to go or my dinner will get burned. Take care!"

"Ok, you too. Don't go out after, it's too late."

"We'll see. Bye! Don't fight with anyone tomorrow..."

"Bye."

Even though I didn't want to admit it, I was starting to enjoy all the attention he was giving me. And every time we met, he looked adoringly at my forehead as he tried to persuade me to date. But every time I was about to give in, conversation would inevitably turn to Mahmoud, the club, and his nonsense stories of how his deep love for me brought him trouble.

As I saw it, the full story amounted to a cock competition to see who could get close to me first. The Stubborn Engineer fancied me, and apparently Mahmoud, the owner of Club Istanbul, fancied me too. Or perhaps, Mahmoud was motivated by a desire to piss off the Stubborn Engineer far more than by his passions for me. I knew there was more to the story, involving other girls before my time and some gambling issues, as Asrat had heard in the club. But all of those details were conveniently left out of the epics that featured him as their hero. As he saw it, he was embarked in a never-ending odyssey to fight for my heart.

One evening after dinner, I'd had enough of his Mahmoud nonsense. "I don't know why you keep telling me this story," I burst out, and he looked up from the coffee he was preparing. "How will I ever know if you really like me or if you are just playing to win against Mahmoud?

"What?" he looked at me in horror.

"Each new piece of information you reveal, I mistrust you a little bit more," I said, nudging him out of the way and taking over the coffee making.

TORTURE LIST FOR THE

Stubborn Engineer *

1

Walk, walk, walk, walk non-stop for hours.

Most foreigners are not used to walking in Yemen. They are scared of being in the street, are too posh for that, or simply don't know their way around. That includes the Stubborn Engineer. But Bilma and I were always walking or taking shared mini-buses. It was our hobby. And it was even more enjoyable if the pair of the Stubborn Engineer and Mr. Architect were reluctantly and grim-faced accompanying us. We enjoyed our discovery walks and at that time Yemen was much safer for foreigners than it became later. That said, even in those early days, a walk through the streets of Sana'a still provided a nice dose of adrenaline.

2   Gifts of flashing toys.

I loved to give The Engineer balloons, little inflatable balls, colorful eggs with sweets inside, and the best... flashing toys, preferably as pink and girlish as possible. Anything appropriate for a 3-to-5-year-old kid. It was by far my favorite torture for the Stubborn Engineer. Since they were gifts, he could not refuse them and had to carry them around for the rest of the day while we engaged in torture number one: walking. I loved to watch him awkwardly carrying his little trinkets as he tried to decide whether to be happy he'd received my gift or embarrassed that he had been given a pink piece of junk meant for a child.

3   Being taken to very shitty local places that only served sugary tea and beans.

The dirtiest the better, no fancy sushi.

4   Ignored calls (five time minimum).

It became a habit of mine to wait to answer the phone until five consecutive missed calls. "Oops, sorry! I didn't see you were calling me," I'd then said in an innocent voice.

5

To greet everyone I knew when out together.

When going to a restaurant or club with him, I would greet everyone I knew. This was something Mr. Stubborn could not stand. If you go with him to a place, you are his girl, and that meant no random talking with other people. For me, it is simply impolite not to go and say hello to people I know. To make my point, I would not only go and say hello, I would sit and talk with them for at least 20 minutes.

*I recognize that I am a monster, I fully admit it. What can I say? He brought out this side of me.

CHAPTER 13

Happy birthday! I texted the Stubborn Engineer at 6:30 a.m. It was the time I knew he woke up to go to work. I wanted to be the first one to send him birthday wishes. He replied after a few minutes and I called him to wish him a super merry happy birthday again. I was sleepy, but I sang him the happy birthday song in a full energetic voice. He laughed and seemed to enjoy my Broadway-worthy performance.

"Babe, later we do something, eh? I don't know the plan yet, but we celebrate," he said. His voice was happy, which made me happy.

"Count me in... but I am not your babe." I said, laughing.

He texted a few hours later. *8 p.m. Thai resto for informal party with the guys. Bring Bilma.*

Tamam, not a bad choice! I texted back. The Thai restaurant was the only restaurant in town that allowed customers (99% of whom were foreigners thanks to the more than excessive prices) to bring their own bottles of illegal alcohol to drink with dinner.

I left the office earlier than usual so I'd have enough time before dinner to go and buy him a birthday gift. Not a torture trinket, but a good one, a real one. Usually, I am very bad at buying gifts. I never know what to get and find it impossible to guess other people's tastes. This time was different, I knew exactly what I wanted to buy, I just wasn't sure where to find it. Heavy smoker that he was,

I wanted to buy him a lighter and ashtray set wrapped in black leather that I'd seen in a shop. It was very manly and a bit mafia-style, which I knew he would love. The problem was, I couldn't remember where I'd seen it. I knew it would make him happy, and I was determined to find it for him. I looked at my watch. I needed to find it and get home with enough time to change and get pretty so that, for once, I wouldn't be late.

I checked a couple of shops my colleagues had recommended with no luck. I canvased the city, walking, taking several taxis, and a minibus. Just when I was about to give up, I found it; the perfect black leather lighter and ashtray set, presented in a nice metal box. I was so happy that I couldn't hide my grin from the salesman, effectively eliminating my bargaining power. It didn't matter, the shopkeeper was so amused by my enthusiasm that he laughed and gave me a good discount anyways.

Back home, Bilma and I rushed to get ready, tumbling into a taxi and arriving at the restaurant just in time. Mr. Engineer and his friends weren't there yet, so the waitress led us to the private table he had reserved. He had said it would be a casual get-together, but the table was set up with name tags at each place setting, like at a wedding.

Bilma and I start looking at all the names and began to panic. The table had been set boy-girl, boy-girl, couple style. It seemed that I was to play the role of the birthday boy's significant other, sitting on a throne next to Mr. Engineer, while Bilma would be the date for Mr. Engineer's best friend.

Bilma had recently discovered that the Architect was having an affair with one of the stewardesses in Expat House at the same time as he was seeing her, and she was still nursing her wounds. A new Turkish contractor from the same crowd around her was too much on her plate. I clenched my teeth in irritation, but just as we turned to look for an exit, Mr. Engineer and the other invitees arrived. It was too late for Bilma and I to escape. His best friend pulled out a chair for Bilma and sat down next to her. One of his colleagues who had recently gotten married sat next to his Filipino wife, who had invited another Turkish-Filipino couple from Expat House. The women were the sugary sweet, pinky, giggly kind of girls whose cutesy made me want to vomit. I sighed and took a seat, accepting that it was my destiny to spend the evening surrounded by Macho Men and Barbie Dolls.

As the dinner progressed, I began to imagine that an actual Barbie Doll might make better company. The women sat like mannequins—not talking, not eating, not blinking—moving only to pet their respective boy's shoulder and serve them food. *Oh, my boy makes a joke. I laugh, but not too loud!* I imagined them thinking. *Another boy makes a joke. It is not my boy talking. I do not react.* I watched the waiter make his way around the table and I continued to make up conversations for the dolls. *I will ask my boy to order it for me. I cannot do it myself.* Their mouths seem to be used exclusively to support their men with a mild laughter, which they covered with their hands, lest their teeth be seen. Bilma had complained about this sort of behavior among the Expat House crowd when she had been seeing Mr. Architect, but I'd assumed she was exaggerating. I spent the first twenty minutes of dinner watching them as if they were stars in a reality television series. I had never seen anything so pathetic.

After thirty minutes, I came out of my stupor. Bilma was behaving normally, and I began to act more like my usual loud and sarcastic self. I teased Mr. Engineer, but more gently than usual, since it was his birthday. I drank whiskey like the boys, while Bilma sipped herbal liquor and girls primly sipped bubbly pink Prosecco. Mr. Engineer's friends seemed baffled by Bilma and I, but we didn't care.

Finally, it was cake time! A big chocolate cake was placed in front of the Birthday Boy, topped with 29 blazing candles. "Help him blow them out," one of his friends said.

"Yes," grinned his girl. "So romantic!"

I wanted to disappear.

"What is your birthday wish?" Another one asked.

Mr. Engineer looked at me and laughed. "If I say it, it will not come true," he winked, still staring at that particular spot on my forehead. I felt a pit in my stomach, shooting a glance at Bilma, who had finished the whole bottle of herbal liquor and seemed to actually be enjoying her assigned companion. Birthday or not, I didn't want to play happy Barbie and Ken with Mr. Engineer.

"I have a gift for you," I whispered.

"Please do not embarrass me in front of all my friends," he said under his breath.

I pulled out a small toy filled with sweets from my bag. It was not pink, and it was not flashy. Everyone laughed amiably. The Barbies cooed that it was *very sweet*.

Finally, it seemed the party was over. The Barbies and Macho Men stood to leave. I am not a Barbie, and neither is Bilma, so the four of us waved goodbye and then headed north towards the perfectly tacky Mermaid hotel to finish our bottle of whiskey next to the dolphin-shaped swimming pool. We blew cigarette smoke into the night sky. Everyone seemed more relaxed. Bilma disappeared, reappearing minutes later.

She pulled me to the side. "I accidentally made a new pool," she slurred, clearly tipsy. I told her to sit and chill while I went to investigate. I found the tap had broken on the sink and water was flooding the washroom. I closed the water to prevent further damage and returned to the group. Bilma and Mr. Engineer's best friend were flirting, lost in their own world for two.

I shook my head, laughing, and took a seat next to the Birthday Boy.

"Everyone was happy at the party, right?" he asked.

"Yeah, sure," I said, pouring more whiskey into his glass.

"Everyone but you, everyone but us," he said bitterly.

I didn't know what to say. He was right and there was nothing I could do about that. I pulled out his real present and handed it to him.

"Happy birthday," I said. "I hope you like it."

He looked surprised and slowly opened the box. "I love it," he said, a smile brightening his face.

100% right! Chapeau! Bravo! I cheered myself silently.

A waiter came to inform us that they would close soon.

"Let's jump in the pool," Bilma grinned as he walked away.

"Why not," I said, jumping up and taking the Engineer by the hand. "Okay, three, two, one!" The four of us jumped in with a big splash.

"Get out! Mister, it is not allowed! Miss please, the swimming pool is closed!" the waiter ran back to yell at us.

We dragged ourselves out of the water before he got angry enough to call the security guards and we walked home soaking wet.

Bilma and the friend stumbled off to her room, leaving Mr. Engineer and I alone on the couch. We sat face-to-face. "My girl" he said, caressing my hair. "My beautiful girl".

For once, I didn't correct him.

"Happy birthday," I whispered, leaning forward to kiss him instead.

I pulled back in horror. After all the build-up, all the convincing... he was such a terrible kisser! What had I done to deserve such a cruel twist of fate?

HOW TO TAKE
A Minibus
in Yemen

What follows is a quick tutorial to help you understand how the public transportation system works in Yemen. The first thing to note is that there is no public transport.

There are hundreds of private minibuses that act as public transport on fixed routes within the city. These minibuses are a bit bigger than a taxi and a bit smaller than a small bus. They are designed to accommodate seven people, but in Yemen they will hold up to 12. There are also no set stops or fixed schedules. The minibuses simply circulate all day long on their respective routes and pick up the passengers along the way.

It might happen that the driver just decides to change the route out of the blue. Don't worry, he is trying to skip traffic. Just wait patiently. Though it will probably take only five minutes to clear the traffic jam, his shortcut will usually take no more than 15 minutes. Patience! Sooner or later he will get back to the route, usually just in time for the next traffic jam.

Knowing this, if you still want to take a minibus, follow the steps below:

Step 1: Go to the closest main street. Whenever a minibus approaches, raise your hand and the driver will stop.

Step 2: Get inside the minibus. This is the point where you need to pay attention.

The minibus has benches on opposite sides facing each other, one in the back and one in front with the back of the bench parallel to the back of the driver. If you are a female, sit on the bench in the back of the minibus. If you are male, sit on the first bench with your back to the driver. The advantage for the female is that you can see the road, which is especially important for those of you who get carsick. The advantage of the male bench is that you do not see the road, which is especially good for those of you who don't handle the sheer terror of all the mad drivers.

Since three people can fit on each bench, it might happen that a married couple sits on the back bench when the male section is full. In this case, the husband will sit next to the window and the wife will sit in the middle seat so another lady can sit in the remaining spot without being next to a man.

If you are female and enter a minibus and, for example, three men are sitting on the male bench and one on the female bench, leaving two more empty seats on the ladies' bench, you can ask him to go to the male section, even though this will require he and the other male passengers to be packed in like sardines. You will then be free to enjoy all your space on the back bench.

SPECIAL NOTE #1: If, for whatever reason, a male sits next to you and tries to harass you, you are allowed to remove your shoe (only, if you are wearing socks, of course! Don't you dare show your pinky toe in public!) and slap him with it. The driver will stop and make him get out.

Step 3: Once on your correct bench in the minibus, there are some rules. If you are a female, keep quiet. Do not move too much, do not look at the other passengers, do not speak a single word, even if you are next to your best girlfriend who you haven't seen for five years.

If you are a male, you have options. You should either chew qat, talk loudly (as loud as you can) on the phone, debate politics with the other male passengers, or do all three of these things at the same time.

Step 4: When you see where you want to stop along the route, let the driver know.

If you are a man, just growl. No need to say any specific word, whatever guttural noise coming out of your mouth will be sufficient to let the driver know you are getting off the minibus and that he better stop or else you will jump out anyways.

If you are a female, do not dare to open your mouth! (Remember step 3?). This is for the public good. Your voice could be so sensual that you could create an accident. To be on the safe side, delicately knock on the windows of the minibus with your ring. The driver will hear it and stop.

If, as it usually happens, he doesn't hear your knocking. Try again slightly lower, and then again, being sure not to break the glass. At some point the driver will notice, or one of the other male passengers sitting on the bench in front of you will notice and produce the guttural sound for you.

SPECIAL NOTE #2: My recommendation, if you are female, start the knocking process at least 400m before the place you want to stop, or you will likely be walking back at least half a kilometer.

CHAPTER 14

Not only was he a terrible kisser, we made a terrible match. The Stubborn Engineer and I had completely opposite personalities. If he said black, I was thinking white. Like sun and moon, day and night, cats and dogs, we never agreed on anything.

Mr. Engineer also had a quality -if I could call it that -which no one in the universe ever had before. He was the one person who could make me angry in an instant. In the past, people could annoy me, or disappoint me, or make me feel bored. But angry? Never. Yet, he could awaken an anger hidden in my blood cells. Toxic and addictive.

Handling our disagreements was what kept us busy. When we were mad at each other, which was often, I would not answer his calls. He would then change tactics and start texting me the exact location and names of the people I was with at any given moment.

Once I sat with Bilma in Smoky Sky, a new shisha place that had recently opened on a side street of Hadda. It was a fancy lounge, outfitted with blue sofa sets and round white tables. My phone beep and I looked down at his SMS. *Nice shisha they have in Smoky Sky; pass Bilma my greetings.* I looked around, but the place was empty except for a table of young locals. A few weeks later, we were fighting again. My phone chimed. *Enjoy Café Mokha with those two guys sitting next to you.* How could he always knew where I was and who I was with?

"He is like a CIA agent, with the most boring mission ever," I laughed to Bilma one night after an attempt at a truce had ended with him hanging up, followed by an SMS with my location.

"Oh, so you haven't made up yet?" she said.

"I am not going to waste my credit trying to text him or calling him back to fix his childish behavior," I said.

The phone rang and I answered. "Listen, if you want to get angry, get angry my love! 100% up to you! Enjoy your angry time and don't waste mine." I hung up before he could answer.

But these were only little fights and like clockwork, he called back the next day, and we met later that afternoon as if nothing had happened. These small fights made up a 10:1 ratio in our tumultuous affair. It was like praying the rosary, for each ten small fights, there would be one biggie. The big ones were less common, but far more intense.

One night we were having dinner in Hadda when my Lebanese friends were seated at the table next to ours. I stood to greet them, exchanging the typical three cheek kisses. "If she were your girlfriend, I'd be jealous," the Lebanese teasingly said to the Stubborn Engineer. I looked over to see a look of rage in his eyes.

"Hey, he was only joking," I whispered as I sat back down. It didn't matter that my friend was joking. Khalas! The harm was done. I knew it would be a stormy evening of fights ahead. The Stubborn Engineer became mute, silent, not a single word came from his mouth for the rest of dinner. He simply sat with that furious look in his eyes. After our plates were cleared, I'd had enough.

"I'm going, and it is over." I said, standing to leave him at the table.

"What?" he nearly shouted.

As I was about to climb into a taxi, he grabbed me and pulled me back onto the street corner.

"What is your problem?" I said, trying not to shout. "Look, we have been on a few dates, but you are not my boyfriend, you are not my husband, you are not my father; and even if you were, this would be unacceptable."

"You are my girl," he said, leaning close to me. "You will be mine, no matter what you say, I have decided it and I will not stop till I convince you of that."

My mind was spinning. What was wrong with him? Why would he want me, the free spirit, the woman who made him as angry as he made me? It was ridiculous. "I am not the girl you are looking for" I shrugged. "We don't click."

When I looked up again I saw a fury come over his face, transforming it from beautiful to demonic with rage. His fists clenched and I stepped back. Before I had a chance to be really afraid, he relaxed, seemingly back in control of himself. "Want it or not, you are my girl," he replied. "You are the only one for me."

CHAPTER 15

One week passed with no news from Mr. Engineer, not even a single text message. It was weird, as angry as I still was at him, after months of receiving daily texts and calls I found myself missing the messages that said practically nothing, *Hey, what's up? Babe?*, my geolocations after fighting, or even our phone calls full of silences.

The weekend came and I received an unexpected call. Mahmoud wanted to inform me that his club was reopening the following week. It had been closed for some months, but he had regained the license. It would be more accurate to say that he had regained the license to re-open the legal restaurant that housed his illegal club. But I wasn't about to split hairs. His announcement meant that Metropolis would soon be closed in the normal dynamic of Sana'a, where only one club was open at a time. Bilma and I decided a night out was warranted to say our farewells to Metropolis.

The following weekend, I'd still had no word from the Stubborn Engineer. I refused to text him. Stubborn him, stubborn me. On Thursday night, when Mahmoud called again to invite Bilma and all our friends to the grand re-opening of Club Istanbul, I was angrier than I'd ever been at the Engineer, and I wasn't sure that I was in a partying mood.

"Maybe," I told him. "Bilma and I are going for shisha, but maybe after."

We walked towards Hadda Road, the poshest street in Sana'a. I wanted to have a well-deserved white grape shisha after a long and tiresome week. A block away from the lounge, I heard a friendly shriek behind me. "*Habibti!*" a voice called.

I turned to see Sarah, surrounded by her Syrian friends. I'd met Sarah briefly years earlier during my first trip to Yemen. She was half Yemeni half Somali, and since she had a Somali passport, she was allowed to rent her flat alone, with no husband or father living with her, which was something that was forbidden for Yemeni ladies. When I'd moved to Yemen, she'd hosted me for my first month while I looked for accommodations and we'd become good friends.

Though she had some family in Sana'a, her close relatives were all in Aden in the South, which gave her a great deal of freedom. That said, even when she was free from prying eyes, she felt conflicted, alternating nights out dancing at the club and attending expat parties, with long stretches of time when she'd cloister herself at home like a "good Yemeni girl". It seemed that night, she was indulging the former, and she eagerly agreed to join us for shisha.

"*Habibti,* I missed you! Are you coming to dance with us tonight, right?"

"Where are you heading?" I asked, knowing there were only two options.

"Club Istanbul," she said enthusiastically. "You probably heard it was re-opened?"

"Sure, why not," Bilma answered for both of us.

"We were there last week, and it was okay, except for the gate guards," one of the Syrian boys shrugged.

"Oh, I thought it was re-opening tonight," Bilma whispered. "Didn't Mahmoud invite us for the opening night party?"

"Strange," I said. "But Mahmoud only speaks Turkish and Arabic, and my level of Arabic is not that good, so I must have misunderstood him."

I had a bad feeling about going to Club Istanbul, and the mix-up with Mahmoud made me even more wary. The club was practically next to the Stubborn Engineer's house and it was the last place I wanted to see him.

"I'm so excited," Bilma grinned. "I need a night out."

I smiled weakly. At least Mahmoud was on the Engineer's "enemies" list, which made it unlikely he would be there.

"Did you hear what happened to those Russians who were also dancing there?" Sarah said, shaking her head.

"No, what happened?" I asked.

"Remember the men who were always hanging out with Mama Coco girls?" I vaguely remembered them. "They were shot at in their villa in the diplomatic area last week."

"Are they diplomats?" I asked, as shocked that diplomats would be so blatant in keeping company with working girls as I was that they had been targeted. Yemen had slowly become more violent over the last few months.

"No, no," Bilma said. "They were oil contractors."

"I wonder who they pissed off so much," Sarah said. "One was injured, but they are okay. They were so afraid, they just packed their bags and left Yemen."

"Maybe an affair with a local girl, and the family wanted revenge?" one of the Syrian boys guessed.

"Who knows ..."

"So, are you sure we will get into the compound tonight," one of the other boys asked.

"Let me call Mahmoud," I said. "He invited us anyways."

When he answered, I told him that we would be three girls and four boys. I expected him to tell us to leave the boys behind, but instead, he was unusually gracious. "Yes sure, my dear," he said. "You will have no problem at the gate. I will call them now to tell them you are coming, just say my name when you arrive."

As promised, we had no issues at the entrance to the compound. All the guards on evening duty received bribes from Mahmoud. It was a clever way for him to control who was able to enter the club, aside from the residents at Expat House. If Mahmoud wanted someone inside, they would get inside. If he didn't, then it would all come down to bribes. Bribing the guards' supervisor was a fairly sure way to gain access. When we entered the club, I greeted Mahmoud. "Thank you for calling the gate for us," I said.

"Of course," he grinned. "And how beautiful you are today."

I smiled and inched passed him, rushing towards the bar to greet my favorite Somali working girls. Nina, a gorgeous, skinny dancer gave me a couple kisses and her friend Dior shouted a greeting from across the room. Then I felt the big strong arms of Mama Coco as she hugged me.

"Look who is here, I didn't see you in ages, where were you hiding?" she thundered.

"Mama! So happy to see you, you look fabulous as always," I said. "How are you all doing?"

"Better now that we can make some money, girl We were not allowed to that stupid Metropolis club." She stuck out her voluptuous lips in a pout. "Hey, where are your other friends? The sexy beardy ones?"

"Bilma's friend left last month, Sana'a was not for him," I said.

"And your boy?" she nudged me.

"Oh, he was never mine," I winked.

I spotted a few of his friends across the room and was grateful the Engineer was not among them. I waved at them.

"Okay, time to get to work," Mama said. I waved at her and continued my rounds, saying a quick hello to Ali, the best DJ in Sana'a, and a few of the other girls before returning to Bilma, Sarah and our Syrian friends.

Mahmoud stopped at our table to offer us a drink on the house. The Syrian guys had already bought a bottle for the table, but we accepted Mahmoud's drinks, too. The mood was jovial.

"Time to dance," I announced, trailing Sarah and Bilma behind me. The music pulsed and carried us away as we swayed and sang along to the best hits of the summer. Katy Perry kissed a girl and we prepared ourselves to dance to the Beyonce song that always followed. Instead, the DJ put on an Ethiopian tune I had no idea how to dance to.

"Well, time for a break?" I laughed, turning towards the table just in time to see Mr. Engineer entering the club. His eyes flickered over me and he forced a proud smile. Then he did something strange. I watched as he made his way around the room, greeting every single person he knew, including his "enemies." It was a move that seemed as out of character as the big fake smile plastered on his face.

The Amulet

Everywhere I go I carry an amulet. I keep it in my purse in one of the small compartments where you usually put one of your multiple credit, debit, supermarket, or gym membership cards. It is not a religious image or symbol. It is a piece of red and yellow paper cut in the shape of a triangle. Bilma gave it to me on one of our craziest adventures.

There is a place in Yemen scarier than any other, a region deep in the center of the country where not even Yemeni dare to go: Marib, the site of the country's fiercest tribal wars. It's one of Al Qaeda's notorious strongholds. It's also home to the most beautiful archeological sites in Yemen. Marib is the capital of the ancient kingdom of Saba, and it is the only place one can see the prominent temple of Barran, Throne of Belqish, and the Great Dam whose breach is mentioned in the Holy Quran as the cause of the end of one of the greatest ancient civilization. Any one of them would be a dream to see.

Bilma and I had wanted to go for a long time, but we had never found the means. It was problematic even to mention the idea of going to Marib to some of our Yemeni friends and colleagues, who thought we were joking or ignorantly unaware of what it was. Then, one day, Bilma found a way.

We had training workshop at the office for the field staff. I was busy with some other tasks, but Bilma decided to attend. I could hear the voices of ladies talking and laughing in the female coffee area during the training break. The laughter was in reaction to a few words coming out of Bilma's mouth. She couldn't speak Arabic fluently, just enough to make herself understood and understand the words she needed. A few minutes later, Bilma rushed into my office with great excitement. "Come, come, come... fast, to the cafeteria, before the break ends." I followed her. Bilma started with the presentations. "She is Rana, from Al Jawf; Nawal from Ibb, Reem from Shabwah, and she is Sumeyah from Marib. Sumeyah has agreed to take us there next weekend," she said triumphantly.

It was as easy as that. We exchanged telephone numbers and agreed that we would contact each other to plan a trip for the following weekend.

One week passed and to our surprise, Sumeyah called right on schedule to see if we were still available and enthusiastic about the trip. Of course, we were!

The secretary at our office secretly helped us fix all the details of the trip. Sumeyah's cousin had to pick us up and we were supposed to travel in a shared pick-up completely covered and unnoticed until our arrival to Sumeyah's village. We had no permits and only Linda, the office secretary who I highly trusted to have our backs, knew about our plans. We agreed to send her the plate number of the cousin's car as soon as we saw it, so if anything happened, at least she would have some clue as to where to start looking for us. Bilma, for the first and last time in my life, was worried enough to tell me to write something on a piece of paper stating that we were solely responsible for our trip. We slipped the papers, copies of our passports, and a list of emergency contacts back in our homelands into an envelope.

Everything was ready when pick-up day arrived. We covered up, walked to the place where a car was waiting for us and met Sumeyah's cousin (if that's who he really was). We got into a car already stuffed with four men and a driver. Thus, began our trip to fearsome Marib.

As the car neared the outskirts of Sana'a, I could tell we were both scared. We sat in the front seat next to each other and didn't speak, but I tried to cover Bilma's impressive eyes every time her *niqab* shifted. I could feel our hearts racing, muscles tense. Not even 15 minutes into our journey, the driver slammed on the brakes. Our wheels squealed and for a few seconds we were in the opposite lane driving straight into oncoming traffic. The car in front of us had almost run over someone crossing the road, swerving to miss him, and prompting the reaction of our driver.

I imagined the guy getting run over by the car and us smashing into it from behind. Only a few milliseconds had separated us from the disaster. The driver started the engine again. Five hours of sand and silence still separated us from Marib.

Bilma started digging in her purse and finally took out a yellow and red triangle of paper. She handed it to me. "Take this, it will protect you," she whispered. I could tell she meant it with all her heart. I slipped it into my purse.

We crossed check point after check point, each of them controlled who knows by which group or tribe. There were so many that I lost count. The zigzagging road went deep into rocky mountains. Bilma felt asleep, exhausted from too much adrenaline at the beginning of our trip. Despite our initial scare, the drive went on smoothly and when we reached Marib's capital, Sumeyah was waiting for us with two of her two brothers.

They carried AK-47s over their shoulders and stood in front of a pick-up. We climbed in the back seat and were off again. We drove through the city, crossing a couple of neighborhoods on our way to a lake. I had never seen so many weapons and not a single woman in the street. Every man we crossed was visibly carrying a pistol and a Kalashnikov, even very young teens. Sumeyah's eyes were cheerful, barely visible under the narrowly knotted *niqab*, but the brothers were tense. The driver kept glancing up at his mirror, scanning the road behind us. The younger one, wearing glasses and clean shaved face, kept his eyes fixed on the sides of the Hilux. Sumeyah turned to us from the copilot seat and pulled her *abbaya* up to her knees. She was wearing a long, sky blue, silky skirt. She winked and it took me a moment to realize that it was not her skirt that she was showing to us, but two Kalashnikov she'd hidden under her *abbaya*.

On an unpaved road outside of the city, we crossed a new checkpoint. The brothers greeted the men while we kept our gaze down. The moment the check point was behind us, the brothers began to relax. Warm, welcoming smiles appeared on their faces. Thought they couldn't speak a word of English, they had so much fun communicating with us in Arabic for kids. We figured out that we were heading the lake, which turned out to be a man-made modern dam. The weather was so fantastic that we enter the water, fully dressed in abbaya and niqab, wading up to our knees. Sumeyah led the way.

Near the truck, Sumeyah's younger brother picked some pink flowers from a bush and gave one to Sumeyah, one to

Bilma, and one to me before tucking one into the scarf he was wearing wrapped around his head. It was quite a look, the flower in the foreground and the Kalashnakov rising from behind his ear. The brothers were nice and funny.

Bilma started a photshoot – lake, close *niqab*, kalash, open *niqab*, lake, brothers, flower – we ended up with an entire album's worth of images. Our black *abbayas* contrasted dramatically with the turquoise water. When we'd finished, Sumeyah spread out a square tablecloth and start mixing cans of tuna with cucumber and mayonnaise, she placed them in the center of a square plastic foil along with bread and Miranda soft drinks. As we ate, I tried to explain I wanted to see the temple.

"La, la, arhabeen, bunduk," said the oldest one, simulating an explosion with his two hands and laughing.

The other looked down and pulled petals from his flower. It seemed that the temple was now home to some uninvited Al Qaeda inhabitants who were using it as training camp. Not even Maribians could go there.

Lunch was almost over when distant gunfire started on the far bank of the lake. It was time to leave. We headed to Sumeyah's village, which consisted of two small clusters of houses connected by a single road and surrounded by fields. The entire village came out to greet us. So many little kids hugged us and jumped around overexcited. It was rare to see outsiders and they'd never seen foreigners before in their village. To my surprise, the ladies also came to greet and they were not wearing *abbaya* or *niqab*, only their colorful tunics and hijabs. When I asked Sumeyah, she explained that the village was so small that they were all related to each other, one big family, there was no need for covering.

That night, the ladies drew elaborate henna designs on our hands and arms. It seemed that every lady in the village was present at Sumeyah's family house. We spent the night laughing, gossiping, and dancing. Early in the morning, Bilma and I slept in Sumeyah's bed, the only bed in the house.

The next day, Bilma took her camera and started taking portraits of all the kids. All the adults started requesting she take pictures of them as couples and it became a village photo shoot.

Soon it was time to head back to Sana'a. We still had a long journey ahead. A round of hugs from the ladies. The kids were so sad we were leaving, it was almost as if we were already part of their great big family. I saw a little tear forming in Sumeyah's little brother's eye as he gave each of us another flower before placing his in the scarf around his head.

As we drove away, I decided that experiencing the warmth of Sumeyah's family was far better than a visit to the temple. I reached into my purse and felt the triangle of paper. I smiled under my niqab. Our adventure had gone smoothly from the moment Bilma had given it to me. Coincidence? Maybe. But ever since then, I always carried it with me, my little amulet.

CHAPTER 16

I stood by our table, waiting to face Mr. Engineer. He pushed past me to greet Bilma and Sarah with kisses on their cheeks. He shook the hands of the Syrian men and then turned and looked me in the eyes before walking past me to his own table.

"No way," I said under my breath. "It doesn't go like that." He had disrespected me, and I was determined to become his worst nightmare in retaliation. I headed to the bar to order another round, stopping to thank Mahmoud for the shots. I squeezed his arm before walking up to the bar. I ordered two cranberry vodkas for the girls and one gin tonic for me. Mr. Engineer appeared next to me and I turned to him. "I think we should say hi, right?" I said.

"You are kidding, right?" he snarled. "Are you doing this on purpose? Trying to seduce all my enemies or what?"

I moved closer to whisper in his ear. "You know me, you greet me," I hissed, gripping his arm. "It is fucking politeness. Do you understand?"

"And in my fucking house," he said, ignoring my words as he spiraled deeper his paranoid rant. "Well done, well done ..."

I knew one of us was speaking about cats, the other about dogs, but I didn't care. I was going to say my piece. "Never do that to me again," I said, dropping his arm. I snatched our drinks and walked away.

The exchange had lasted only seconds, but it had been so tense that when I returned to our table, one of the Syrian guys looked concerned. "Are you okay?" he asked. "What was that about at the bar?"

"Nothing," I replied. "Only greeting an old friend."

Everyone was happy that night. Bilma, Sarah and the Syrians; the friends of the Architect; the Somali ladies and their clients, everyone danced and laughed. No one was as overjoyed than Mahmoud. I watched him watching Mr. Engineer, an evil smile on his face, and I realized that he had orchestrated our fight.

I could see it clearly. I had been a pawn in his battle with Mr. Engineer. Mahmoud had called the Stubborn Engineer for a "truce" the weekend before, inviting him to Club Istanbul. Mr. Engineer was suspicious and thought it was a setup. He assumed I would be there. Maybe he'd imagined finding me sitting at Mahmoud's table. Whatever his reason, he didn't accept Mahmoud's invitation, instead sending some friends for opening night. Mahmoud had planned on this. That's why he had invited me for the following week, when Mr. Engineer would have let down his guard and accepted Mahmoud's olive branch. Club owners are known for their knowledge of human behavior, and Mahmoud certainly had us pegged. He probably had hoped Mr. Engineer's temper would explode at some point and he would start a fight with one of the guys, but he got something even better; a bitter, public argument between us.

I should have known Mahmoud had ulterior motives when he'd invited my friends, both girls and boys, making a distinction he had never made on previous occasions. I sat fuming, trying to decide who I was angrier with. I finally resigned myself to the fact that Mahmoud was who he was, and so was Mr. Engineer for that matter. Maybe I only had myself to blame.

A few weeks later he appeared in front of my office with two big boxes of donuts, one for me and one for my team.

We didn't talk about the fight, or the month of silence, instead, we stubbornly continued pushing and pulling one another through the steps of our dangerous dance.

THE DISAPPEARANCE OF A FISH
(Ode to Bilma)

Slowly, but steadily, the fish occupying my sight starts to disappear. It is whole: head, skin, meat, bone.

A couple of minutes pass and the shape is not precise anymore, it has started to vanish. The meat starts to diminish; the white is getting less and less every time, letting the grey skin stand alone in the middle of the dish. But by matter of solidarity, or simple fish anatomy, the grey runs away to catch up with the first white parts. Easier to split apart. Not a fish anymore, not anymore what it used to be.

The bone, that magnificent stable and consistent structure dividing the body equally, rests in the middle, but suddenly, a crunch, and the piece is not there anymore. Where did it go? What has happened to that impressive natural ladder? Spine by spine, bone by bone, crunchy and flavorful, it is also gone. Not a fish anymore, not anymore what it used to be.

And the corpse lies bodyless in the middle of the dish, amputated, helpless. Only the solitary head remains. But the feast is not finished yet. The best is yet to come. And it starts with the cheeks—soft, juicy, mellow cheeks. Not a head anymore, not what it used to be.

Like a skull, the perforated head looks at the empty ceiling with a haunting lifeless gaze. Not for long, because the eyes will also soon fall victim to the banquet. And suddenly there is no longer swollen white eyes, only space, transparent, infinite. Not a head anymore, not anymore what it used to be.

The dish is empty, as if nothing had ever been there. Not even a trace of the feast. Not a fish anymore, not anymore what it used to be.

CHAPTER 17

Despite my best efforts, and his efforts too, the sweet donut reconciliation lasted for 14 days. After that, I didn't see him at all for three months. I was very angry at him and he was equally angry at me. Love and hate, so far and so close. Then came the party, and with it, the news.

He was finally leaving Yemen. I put on my best poker face and congratulated him. It was ironic. When we broke up, I was the one who had decided I didn't want to see him again. I thought that without him, my life in Yemen would become easier. It would certainly be easier to abide by my rule: "Stay away from toxic people". It was advice I always gave to my friends, yet had been slow to implement myself. But that day, when I learned he was leaving, I felt sad.

So many things had changed in the three months since we ended our doomed relationship. Bilma had left Yemen for good on the day we broke up. Anna had moved in. It was her idea to have a housewarming party, and her crazy idea to invite The Stubborn Engineer.

"Can I invite Mr. Stubborn to the party?" she'd asked a few days earlier.

"Up to you," was my reply. "I don't want to see him and I haven't talked to him for more than three months, but it is also your house, so if you want to invite him, go ahead." With an answer like that, I never thought she would. And I never imagined he would come. But I had been wrong.

When he walked in the party, my heart jumped and I momentarily forgot why we had gone more than three months without speaking. Then I remembered how it all ended.

The week Mr. Stubborn and I reconciliated was the week of Bilma's farewell party, so Sarah, Anna and I called Mahmoud to ask him if he could lend us his club for a private party just for us girls. Since the Stubborn Engineer house was in the same compound, I planned to go to Expat House to visit him before the party. *I pass by yours before Bilma's party?* I texted. He wrote back. *OK. Call when you are in compound.*

Sarah, Anna and I head to Expat House with a big bag full of balloons and decorations. Bilma couldn't leave without a colorful party! The girls went to club to prepare the decorations for the party and I went to see Mr. Engineer. When he opened the door, I could tell something was wrong.

"You are really going to that place alone?" he snarled. "That fucking club?"

"Yes, I told you...it's Bilma's farewell party."

"So, Mahmoud invited you, right?" he said, pacing the room. "You are so stupid; don't you see what he wants?"

"No, actually, he didn't," I said, getting angrier by the minute. "We called him to ask if we could do the party there."

"And who called? You?"

I skipped the question. "It is a private party, only the girls."

"Yes, of course, sure," he said. He walked over and stared in my eyes. "Listen, I will not repeat this to you. If you go to that party, you and me, it's over."

I was shocked. I'd never imagined he would give me an ultimatum. Especially not involving Bilma, my BFF, my buddy, my fellow adventurer, my sidekick! My rage grew. Who did he think he was to threaten me like that? No,

I shook my head, I would not allow him to blackmail me. If I allowed it once, I would sooner or later be blackmailed again. "Don't make me do that, you know Bilma is..." I warned.

"Up to you. You choose. The party or me."

When I arrived to the Club, Mahmoud politely asked if I had anyone else I would like to invite. "Even one here in the compound...there is no problem," he said.

"No need," I shook my head. "I'm only here with my girls."

Top 10 Things
to do in Sana'a

√ Chew qat (no way I can change this one!)

√ Take a minibus and enjoy the ride!

√ Eat beans for breakfast with sugary tea

√ Listen to Yemeni music and count the words: My life (*hayati*), my love (*habibi*), and my soul (*ya rouhi*) until you reach 1,000 (per song)

√ Kill invisible genies with an AK-47 charged with Albanian bullets

√ Get driven around by a Yemeni who owns a car (Either really, really slow or really, really fast)

√ Go crazy and choose the weirdest shisha flavor available (Coca-cola, anyone?)

√ Bargain for hours and get stressed about it

√ Try to read a book by candlelight when the power is off

√ Eat beans (again) for dinner with sugary tea, followed by a nice qat chew (Congrats you have started the loop again!)

CHAPTER 18

I stood on the terrace of the new house Anna and I shared. The party was in full swing with a good mix of Yemenis and expats enjoying the evening. I was talking to some Spanish soldiers and enjoying a glass of Rioja, when suddenly Anna passed her phone to me.

"Can you talk to them?" she asked. "They don't know where our new house is, give them directions."

Them? Them, who? I thought, taking the phone. I immediately recognized the voice. It was the Stubborn Engineer. My mind raced. I was in no mood to see him. *What if he caused a scene?* I sighed. *What could I do?* I gave him directions and opened the door when the bell rang. There he was, as stubborn and stroppy as always. In that split second, I forgot our painful ending, and in the next moment, memories of our disastrous end came flooding back. The tension was so high you could cut it with a knife, but I plastered on a smile and greeted he and his friend. He slightly nodded as a reply and I left them to return to my other guests.

While everyone at the party was talking to each other, discovering new people and enjoying the night, Mr. Engineer and his friend stood in a corner drinking their bottle of whiskey and having a hushed conversation in Turkish. I watched him, thinking that he was being rude. Same old. But I decided not to let it ruin my day. When guests started to leave, Mr. Engineer and his friend slowly joined the remaining group. A few more people left, and the Stubborn Engineer was suddenly beside me.

At some point, we were the only two people left on the terrace. He stared at that fixed point on my forehead and tried to touch my hair. But I didn't give in. I didn't want to go back to daily fights. We still had feelings for each other, but we were incompatible, utterly, deeply incompatible. I told him that, and he seemed to understand. That's when he told me he was leaving.

That day we built a new relationship between us. We started taking care of each other, supporting each other in our everyday struggles to survive in the increasingly aggressive country that Yemen was becoming. His boss postponed his departure. Then he postponed it again.

As his stay in Yemen continued to be drawn out, we continued to talk a few times a week, whenever one of us needed it, not for daily check-ins or accusations, as it had been before. Life in Yemen was becoming a roller coaster. A car exploded in a compound full of expats one month, a foreign journalist was kidnapped the next, and a UN car got shot-up in between. Violence was becoming the new normal. Anna and I started to wear niqab to go back and forth from the office and we no longer used random taxis. We only traveled with drivers we knew. Worst of all was the air of suspicion. Expats had become paranoid and mistrusting of both locals and other foreigners. The world shrank as people began to cluster in fragmented factions.

They say two years is the maximum time one should stay in a place like Yemen without going insane. The Stubborn Engineer had been there much longer. One day, shortly after yet another explosion, he showed up at my door in the middle of the night. I invited him in. He looked destroyed, like a dead body pulling along his soul. He didn't explain. He sat on the sofa next to me and put his head in my lap. He said that he couldn't take it anymore and he started quietly crying. To see him like that broke my heart.

"It's time," I said, stroking his hair. "It's really time to leave Yemen."

Next day he resigned. On our last night, when Mr. Stubborn came to say goodbye, a lightbulb went on in my head. During our time hanging out, dating, and fighting, I never thought to ask him about the weird radio in his kitchen cupboard or how he had always known exactly where I was and who I was with. I had naively assumed his Turkish friends saw me around and reported back to him, but recently, since things had gotten bad, very few people ever left the compound. Yet, he still would call, this time in a joking voice rather than an angry one, to inform me of my exact location and company.

His was not a casual network of friends, but a strategic network of informants. The Stubborn Engineer was not an engineer at all. He was a spy. When I asked him that night, he looked surprised and a bit delighted, like a child who'd gotten caught. As an answer, he simply laughed and kissed his favorite spot on my forehead before climbing into an unmarked black car and waving goodbye.

The Killer
Adventure 3

CHAPTER 19

I kissed a killer. The first time was long before I knew he was one, but I kissed him again even after I knew. It all started one afternoon when the three musketeers — Sarah, Anna and I — went for shisha at one of our habitual places. In typical form, I arrived late. When I walked into the café, I spotted them sipping their cappuccinos at our usual table. My seat, instead of being empty, was occupied by a young, good-looking man. He had fair skin, medium-length dark hair, and hazel eyes. *Good change you have made,* I laughed to myself. *Where have you girls found this cutie to replace me?*

I approached them and the newcomer rose from my chair. "Thank you," I said, taking my seat and smiling at him, full of curiosity. He pulled over another chair and Anna introduced us. They had met a half hour earlier in the kebab place next door, and in addition to asking for some of his extra ketchup, she invited him to join us. I wasn't surprised. Anna had a gift for finding the most random people in the most random places, from ambassadors in secondhand markets to taxi drivers kitting scarfs, and she always added them to her collection of acquaintances. When she mentioned that he was an optometrist by education, he stopped her.

"But I have never practiced," he said so cheerful I wondered for a moment if his sentiment was fake or if he might be mad. Clearly hyperactive, he was a blur of nonstop movement and questions, one after another, asked without pausing to hear a reply. Sarah was less than thrilled with the addition. "I can smell he is not good," she hissed after we left the coffee shop. "He is hiding something."

He became our fourth musketeer. Whenever we called him, he wanted to come with us, no matter the activity. He would laugh and joke and speak about trivial things soon forgotten. Sarah was blessed (and cursed) with the biggest mama heart of us all, and even she warmed to him. It might also have had something to do with her rivalry with Anna, and not wanting to appear petty, as though she didn't like the new crazy boy simply because Anna discovered him.

Then, one afternoon as we sat enjoying tea and shisha before heading to the club, he shocked us all.

"I've been shot three times in my life," he said out of nowhere. He pulled up his peach-colored summer pullover to reveal two round scars, one near his stomach and one near his hip bone.

Sarah blushed and covered her face with her hands in the most Yemeni reaction I'd ever seen from her. Anna was somewhere else that day, and simply ignored him or didn't hear. But I was fascinated, moving my face closer to examine his scars with great attention. My grandfather fought in the war and had a bullet scar on his left thigh. When I was a kid, I was mystified by the strange shape it had left on his skin and I spent long periods of time looking at it and asking him questions about the story behind it. Based on my limited experience with bullet wounds, our fourth musketeer's scars looked like the real deal to me.

"I will not show you the third one, ma Cherie. It would be a scandal," he said and started laughing loudly.

I glanced at Sarah and wondered if she might have been on to something with her initial assessment of the beautiful young man.

"I didn't know that being an optometrist was so dangerous in your country," I said, unable to resist.

"I already told you," he chuckled. "I have never practiced my profession."

"What was your job then?" I asked. "You never did tell us."

"You don't want to know," he replied in a jovial voice.

"Oh, but I am a curious person," I said. Silence. I raised my eyebrows mischievously.

"My dear, you wouldn't be sitting here so comfortably if you knew about my previous job," he said, a daring smile coming over his lips.

"Come on, this is Yemen!" I said, incredulously. "Craziness and normality are twins here."

"Maybe another time," he said, taking a slow sip of his coffee and looking me in the eyes. He was clearly enjoying the game he started.

"Fine, but now you cannot leave the story in the middle," I said, leaning back and taking a long puff of green apple smoke.

"Can't I? *Et c'est à cause de quoi?*" he said, continuing his annoying habit of mixing English and French into his conversations.

"*De la politesse*, you crazy doctor," I said, kicking him gently under the table. "At least tell me how you got shot?"

He laughed, enjoying the attention. "Okay, I will tell you, but only if you dance with me tonight, *une chanson, bas.*"

"Deal," we said and shook hands.

At Club Istanbul we drank and danced until the early morning and all four of us had a great time. We dropped Sarah off at home first, and then he dropped off me and Anna, waving before disappearing into the early morning darkness. I climbed into bed and closed my eyes. My dreams were interrupted by the blaring sound of the worst reggaeton song ever created in the history of music, one whose lyrics I always hoped no one around me would understand. It was, of course, my ringtone.

As a general rule, I always switched my phone off before going to sleep. There is an open debate with half of the population thinking they have to keep their mobiles on 365 days, 5 hours, 48 minutes and 45 seconds per year in case an emergency occurs or one of their friends gets in trouble, but a long list of ill-timed calls from people who always called me when I was sleeping for the most insignificant trifles or utter indecencies, had convinced me to join the other half of the population who appreciate a good sleep, and I always turn off my phone. But, after our night of frolicking, I'd forgotten. I glared at the clock, which read 3:30 a.m.

I didn't want my ringtone to turn Anna's dreams into nightmares, so without looking at the screen to see who the guilty party was, I picked up. "Yes?" I said in a dry voice, stretching out the eeee for emphasis.

"They are coming for me, I know it," a voice slurred. "I need to be cautious." The fourth musketeer was completely drunk. I heard glasses breaking and imagined a small table or chair falling down.

"Hey...hey!" I said, a knot of worry growing in my stomach. "What are you talking about? Are you okay?"

"But how are you my princess, tell me, how are you? You are my princess because you are pure, not like me, I am... I am..." his normal hyperactivity had transformed into acute anxiety as he rambled. "But they will not find me."

"Who are they? Are you in trouble?" I asked.

"Don't worry about me." He said, hardly able to articulate. "Maybe I will need to disappear for some days. You don't know who I am..."

Worried as I was, I was grateful mobile phones only transmit voice, because if they could send smells, his vodka odor would have knocked me down. I opened my mouth to tell him that I didn't need to know, that he needed to have some water and go to bed, but it was too late. In the breath between his monologues, he'd hung up.

BINT-AS-SAHAN

And Other Yummy Yemeni Dishes

Nothing compares to Yemeni food, which it has its own character distinct from any other Middle Eastern cuisine. It is rich, unique and, in my bias opinion, extremely yummy. Yemeni know how to make almost anything they cook delicious, from marinated grilled fish to their national dish, *saltah*, which is a sort of meat, okra and fenugreek stew cooked in a round, black mud pot.

The basics, like a simple bean dish called *fasoulia* are so well prepared, and especially tasty when served with *rashoush*, an amazingly huge round of flat, crispy bread topped with sesame seeds. Add to that all the fresh juices — watermelon, mango, carrot and orange, avocado — squeezed in front of you at small, multi-colored street cafes, and you've got what I would consider the ultimate comfort food.

Shafoot is a dish that fascinates me. As simple as it is to prepare, trust me, this dish can satisfy any food lover. Imagine this, a layer of spongy flat bread called *lahoh* topped with a second layer of chopped tomatoes, cucumbers, and other salad-related ingredients all sprinkled with cumin and lemon. The third and final layer is made of thick, tangy, local yoghurt (yeheeee!). Decorate with some mint leaves, et voila! Your *shafoot* is ready for me to eat.

There is one Yemeni specialty that stands above all others, one that *je completely adore. Bint-as-sahan* literally translates to "the girl of the dish". Why? I have no idea. But it is this girl's absolute favorite. It is the most awesome recipe ever created in the history of human gastronomy. It is made with Hadrami honey, which is not only a pleasure for the palate, but also one of the purest and therefore healthiest honeys in the world, thus removing any guilt one might feel at over-indulging. The honey is a natural remedy, they say will keep you healthy (note for men: it is also considered a source of extra sexual power).

But what is *bint-as-sahan*? Well, it is basically a sort of massive pastry made of multiple thin layers of bready dough baked in the oven and then splashed with black sesame seeds and covered with thick Hadrami honey. It is simply delicious. I don't care if I am fat, if I am on a diet, or if I am about to explode after a copious meal, if there is *bint-as-sahan*, I will eat it.

CHAPTER 20

One day passed, then two days. I tried to tell myself that no news was good news. We three original musketeers sat in a semicircle on the ground surrounded by low cushions with our wooden shisha in the middle like a statue to adore. The Jaima café was a modern place decorated old Egyptian-style, which was contradictory in the sense that most modern things in Yemen were as old-fashioned as the old in Egypt. Still, it was an enjoyable effect, and we sat smoking like *belle models* from an old postcard.

"Good afternoon, my ladies," a familiar voice echoed behind us. "You look particularly adorable today."

"Ohlala, look who is here," Sarah grinned.

I turned my head and saw the fourth musketeer grinning down at us. "Can this humble gallant join this harem and be the envy of the richest sultan?"

We burst into loud, inappropriate-for-Yemen laughter. "Please, be the belle of our ball," I said, waving my arm. My eyes scrutinized his, looking for a trace of remembrance or recognition of the strange call, but there was nothing. He sat grinning like his old self, seemingly without remorse or embarrassment or memory of the call.

Jovial conversations followed, more tea was served, and finally, the charcoal on our shisha burned out and died. After taking a final puff, the fourth musketeer got up from his sultan's couch to leave. "*Mesdames, toujours un plaisir de vous voir.* Anna, Sarah," he said, nodding goodbye to each of them. "My princess," he said. He took my hand and softly, scarcely touching my skin with his lips, kissed it and left.

"What was that? What is going on with him today?" Anna asked.

"He must have been transported by the atmosphere," Sarah laughed. "*Avec plaisir*? My princess," she kept laughing as she continued her particular impersonation of our boy's voice. Anna and I laughed along.

"I'm not ready to go yet, should we order more tea? A shisha refill?" Anna asked.

"Why not?" I said, settling back down into the cushions. I was still amused by his reaction.

Anna waved over the waiter pointing at the dead charcoal on top of the shisha, as Sarah sat playing with her phone. *Princess*? I thought back to that late-night call. It seemed he had remembered more than he let on.

When he called again later that night with the same panic in his voice, I invited him to come over. When he arrived, he refused my offer of chamomile tea and instead took a shot of vodka. He sat on the couch with the bottle still clutched in his hand. "You wanted to know how I got shot, no?"

"It's alright," I said, looking at his pained expression. "Only if you want to tell me."

He nodded and took another shot.

"I was working for the government of my country. When I finished university, I was recruited and started to work for them and I did that for more than four years. I was very young, but they offered me a new house, a car, and a good salary. We had always been quite poor, me and my mum, since my father abandoned us. I don't remember him, but I hated him, and I think my mum did, too. I have no brothers or sisters. When they gave me all that money, I promised to myself I would be loyal to those people, the first ones who had helped me inf life. I brought my mum to my new house and I obeyed them without even thinking for a long time. Then the revolution to overthrow the regime started three years ago."

He barely paused to breath and I found myself holding my breath.

"One day there was a violent protest downtown near my workplace. I was curious so I went to see what was going on. It was still the beginning of the revolution. I was observing the protesters from afar and how they were confronting the police when the gunfire exchange started. I guess someone among the crowd recognized me and knew where I was working. I was shot, once. The bullet passed through my body, but it didn't touch any vital organs." He paused to take another shot.

"I don't know why, but to see those protesters, how they were facing the police knowing that it was completely impossible for them to win, but believing in their cause no matter what? It made me think a lot. Yes, they had shot me, but I knew they were right to do it. All the things they were questioning were indeed the devil of our country. They wanted a clean government, free from corruption and patronage. They wanted equal opportunities for all the citizens. They were citizens like I had been four years before when my mum and I had nothing. When I recovered, I quit my job and joined them."

I didn't ask him any questions. I knew he would tell me what he needed to, no less no more.

"We were hit with tear gas and rubber bullets first, then real ammunition when the protests spread from the capital to the rest of the country. One day, they recognized me. This time the government side. There were snipers in the buildings surrounding the square where we had staged a sit-in. They knew me and they shot directly at me, a bullet from the sky straight to my body. I was their target. Death was my punishment for having changed sides. Everyone ran away when the riot police started charging the crowd. The same sniper who had shot me was right next to me. I could hear his steps, I could see his face and feel his breath. I recognized him from my early days in the government. I was on the ground, blood leaving my body fast. I could feel the warmth of my blood underneath my stomach, making a pool. He shot me again and I died. Or that is what they told me, anyways. When I woke up, I was in an ambulance surrounded by corpses. They thought I was also one, but I opened my eyes. A miracle. I got surgery in a house from one of the doctors supporting the revolution and recovered, but I couldn't go back home, it would have put my mother and her sister, my aunt, in danger, so I crossed the border and after a long journey I ended up here long ago. Now communication has stopped, and I haven't been able to reach my auntie and my mum in three months. The last news I received is that the neighborhood was very badly hit, that it is destroyed, almost inexistent."

He became silent. What I had assumed to be a big ego or narcissistic personality was merely a tough cover hiding a distressed and confused young man unable to reach his only remaining family. He sat next to me with his elbows on his knees, looking at my hand, which he had taken in his as he spoke about his mum. I put my other hand on his shoulder and he suddenly stood up. "I need to go now," he said. I could tell he was holding back tears and didn't want to cry in front of me.

"Hey, wait, stay here for a while," I said.

"My princess needs to sleep. Tomorrow you need to go to work, no?"

"Right, but it's fine..."

"Sorry about that, I didn't want to bother you..." he sounded ashamed.

"Don't say that, you know where I am, you can call me or come here whenever you need to," I said, meaning every word.

We stood in the frame of the main door and he put his cheek next to mine. "My princess, are you going to give me a goodnight kiss before I leave?"

I kissed his rough cheek and closed the door behind him. His story, already twisted and far-fetched, made no sense. A house and a car for a simple civil servant? I didn't doubt that his tale was based on some kind of truth, but I wondered, and worried, about which parts were which and the kind of secrets one must have to make a hired gun shoot a half-dead man twice.

MAMA
COCO
And Co.

Prostitution exists in every corner of the world. Details like the price of the service or the nationality of the girls and customers varies from place to place, as does the legal framework. Is it legal or not? Is the customer the criminal or the businesswoman? Yet, the practice itself remains the same. In Yemen, a highly conservative and poor country, prostitution has a particularly niche market. Despite no one has a coin to buy bread, the community is morally policing your personal life, and qat devastates male sexual performance, the sex trade is fully operational.

I know quite a lot of the girls working on the second rung of the prostitution ladder in Yemen. It all started with Mama Coco, a fat, curvy Somali lady who happens to be an amazing dancer. We met at Club Istanbul when I first came to Yemen and she introduced me to some of the other girls: Dior, Lavan, Nina. Whereas the first rung of the prostitution ladder is mostly made up of local ladies working with local customers for a very cheap price (around 25 USD per service) most of Coco and Co.'s customers are expatriates who will pay 250 USD per service, a rate higher than the average monthly salary in Yemen. And believe me, their agendas are always full.

Add at least one zero and you will get an estimate for the third rung, but you will rarely see the high-class prostitutes in Yemen. These blond Caucasian girls, at the very top of the prostitution market, are never in clubs or cafes, as they only work exclusive private parties for very VIP local customers. The richest of the rich in Yemen will pay thousands for a service.

You'll find Mama Coco with her short dress, big tummy, and sexy moves, along with her other colleagues, at any gathering where there might be potential expat customers. I stepped to help Coco one night when it looked like security was going to throw her out roughly. After that, I put her in a taxi a few times when she was too drunk, because I was scared the police would stop her and take her directly to prison, as had happened with some other girls before. That might be why she seems to love me, greeting me with a warm hug every time we meet.

Mama Coco is always cheerful, despite all the tragedies she carries in her soul. She had to leave Somalia when the war started and her mum, sister and two daughters are still there. She sends them money every week, sustaining the whole family with the money she earns working in Yemen. Her dream is to one day open a beauty salon for a more secure future. "The beauty salon will give me less money than men," she told me one day. "But who will pay for a night with an old toothless lady? And I am getting old..."

I've received plenty of disapproving looks and comments about her from some of my friends. According to them, it is terrible for my reputation to be hugged by her, even more so in public in the middle of a crowded club! Everyone knows her business and could think I am working with her, too! Gasp!

"Who cares?" I always said.

I have no clue where Coco is now, but I like to imagine her in a small, cozy salon full of colors and light. I can see her cutting hair and gossiping with the girls, playing her music at full volume, and wearing a proud smile that says she's finally made it.

CHAPTER 21

At 3 a.m., the world's worst reggaeton song blared from my phone.

"Can I come over?" asked the desperate voice on the other end of the line.

The voice was not only desperate, it was also drunk. I wasn't sure it was a good idea to allow a desperate, drunk and, to a larger extent, unstable man into my house, despite my offer of shelter any time he needed it. After our last conversation, I'd become suspicious.

"It sounds urgent, why don't we speak on the phone right now instead," I said, grasping at the best excuse my sleepy mind could muster.

"They are coming after me, they want me to join them again."

I noticed an echo of metallic as if he were in a stairwell. "Where are you right now?" I asked.

"Don't worry they didn't follow me," he said breathlessly. "I am here in the building."

I jumped at the sound of soft knocking on my front door. Fuck, I thought, pulling a jumper over my small silky pajamas. I opened the door and he stumbled directly over to the sofa, and open a blue bottle of Skyy dangling from his hand. "Come my princess, sit here with me, we will drink together."

I brought two glasses from the kitchen and he poured me a shot before drinking directly from the bottle himself.

I wet my lips with the vodka with no intention of drinking it. I had been fast asleep only minutes earlier and the smell alone was making me dizzy. I didn't want to be drunk with the unknown creature my friend became when he mixed alcohol with memories of his previous life.

"They want me to go back, to join them again. You know I was the best one among them, and now that they are losing, they want to bring me back to help them win. My boss wants me, he is a good man. But I don't want to go back to that. If I don't go, they will kill me if they find me. I am too valuable to be left alive." I felt like a silent doll in front of him as he rambled on, seemingly speaking only to himself.

"Let's drink," he said, pouring another shot into my glass, not realizing it was still completely full. The alcohol seemed to have a calming effect on him, but then he began with even more passion in his voice. "I trust you a lot, you are the only person here in Yemen I trust. That's why I will explain to you who I am. I didn't want to tell you because I didn't want to scare you, but you are my princess. You have to know."

I felt a sinking feeling at the direction our conversation was taking, I disliked the tone and I had a feeling I would dislike it even more after his explanation.

"Do you know what my nickname was? They used to call me Air," he said, almost proudly. "I could go anywhere without being noticed. It was true when I said I worked for the government, but not as a civil servant. After university, I was doing my time in mandatory military service and they saw something special in me and they recruited me for the paramilitary forces of the regime. We were a small but very effective squad. I rapidly rose through the ranks from a nobody to the leader of operations. We chased select targets, raided houses during the night. We would detain or directly kill, depending on our orders. It didn't really matter, the ones we detained disappeared too after being tortured. No one ever returned home once we had entered. But none of that was my business, I just completed my orders."

"Who were the targets?" I asked so calmly it seemed to surprise him. I wasn't scared or shocked.

"All sorts of people, civilians, journalists, students, a lot of political opponents. Anyone considered problematic by the regime."

"And by you?" I asked, with more heat in my voice. "You never thought about who those people were and why they were targeted?"

"It was not my business to decide whether or not they should be targeted. I only had a mission to accomplish."

"Yes, but they were not criminals or armed people, they were only people thinking differently."

"As I told you, that was not my business. I was not there to think, I was there to kill."

"Didn't you feel guilty then? Don't you feel guilty, now?"

"Listen, I never killed a woman or a child," he said. "I told you, I was very good at it, so better I did it than another sloppier one who might cause more damage. I was clean. I only entered, took my target or shot him and left. No mess, no problems, no more victims but him."

"And it was like that for four years?" I still couldn't process everything he was saying. I understood that he was following orders, but for me that excuse was not powerful enough. How could he feel no remorse? It left a bitterness in my mouth. But when I looked up at him, I still saw only my friend. My friend, The Killer.

"For four long years. Until the revolution started and they asked me to do things I cannot even say," he slurred. "I ran away, joined the opposition, got shot and ended up here."

My head hurt. I was confused. I looked out the window. The first sunbeams were appearing on the horizon. "You can sleep here," I said. "Don't leave now."

A man leaving my building at dawn would be too suspicious, and far too much quality material for my gossiping neighbors. I went to bring him water and a blanket. "Have a good sleep. Make yourself comfortable. My house is your house," I said.

"Are you not going to give me a goodnight kiss, my princess?" he asked.

"It is not night anymore."

I woke a few hours later, I began to wonder if the story The Killer had told me had only been a bad dream. I crept downstairs and found that his body had disappeared from the couch. The only evidence of the previous night were the empty bottle of vodka that had fallen to the floor and my little glass, still full on the side table.

A SOCIOLOGICAL EXPERIMENT

In Sana'a

Anna! My lovely Anna is crazy. She is indeed. She has a PhD in Sociology and I think she is simply too clever for this world, though at some point she decided to play dumb and silently enjoy the show.

Anna's social skills are amazing. From the top to the bottom of the social pyramid, she mingles with anyone she finds. Within her close circle of friends there is a cool group of very young Yemeni who started a cultural center, something completely unique and bizarre in Sana'a. They do not come from the typical elite families that are educated outside the country, no, they are made in Yemen and they are awesome. She also has very good taste in men, particularly the wardrobe-sized soldiers who protect foreign ambassadors. Her preference for blonds is apparent in her many friendships with Danish diplomatic bodyguards.

As clever as she is crazy, Anna decided to set up a social experiment in our house one Friday afternoon.

Her Yemeni buddies were not used to foreigners, and her big, blond army boys were not accustomed to being around Yemeni, which may sound strange, but is a common hazard of living inside a compound on constant alert, waiting for an attack. Without previous notice to either group, Anna invited them all to our house for cookies and coffee.

For Anna, bringing people together is the best way to prevent conflict. If different groups of people come to know each other they can see what they share, what they have in common, instead of their differences. If they bond, fear disappears, and with it hate, too. And if the first encounter happens as a surprise, according to Anna, it is even better. "Unexpected amplifies the effect," she explained. "And it's more fun to watch."

The four skinny Yemeni youngsters arrived first. They sat in our garden as we prepared coffee and poured juice. We sat speaking about cinema and music until there was a knock at the door. Our blond buddies had arrived. Anna met them at the door and kindly requested they deposit their guns into our gun storage box at the entrance in keeping with our no-guns-allowed-inside-the-house rule.

When they entered the garden, the surprise was mutual. There was terror on the faces of our little Yemeni friends when they saw the Vikings enter, and the Vikings, too, wore expressions of shock and a little fear. The garden became a tennis court, Yemenis on one side, foreigners on the other, with me and Anna playing referee in the middle with coffee and cookies.

It is completely true that it is the unknown that scares us the most, and, fortunately, one of the youngsters who spoke reasonably good English broke the ice. "Where are you from?" he asked in a quiet, shy voice.

"Denmark" — one of the giants replied.

"Haha, like the butter cookies in a can" — was our Yemeni friend reply.

His simple and easy question and funny reply was enough to start the conversation flowing. In a half an hour the two groups had become one. Our Yemeni friends sat listening, totally delighted, as the blond giants shared stories of wartime adventures in Afghanistan. Big muscles and skinny bones mingled and chatted and drank coffee together the rest of the afternoon.

Watching them, I could not tell who was happier; the Yemeni enraptured by the stories of the foreign giants, or the Danish, having met their first locals who might become friends rather than potential threats. Then I looked over at Anna, who sat watching her handiwork and I knew. She was the happiest of all. *Chapeau!*

There is something funny that happened here, the bodyguards left and after an hour or so, one of them came back. He had forgotten his weapon in our storage drawer! The Yemenis were still there and we all shared a good laugh.

CHAPTER 22

"**I** saw our male musketeer today!" Anna called from the living room as she came in from work.

"Oh really?" I said, walking into the room, trying to sound disinterested. "How is he?". It had been four days since his drunken confession, and I hadn't heard from him.

"Fine, I guess," she shrugged. "He was eating falafel in the corner place with some friends of his."

"The guys we met who are studying medicine?" I asked.

"Yes, the same," she said. "Since when are you so interested in his private life?"

"You know me, I am interested in all private lives," I winked.

"And nothing else to do in Sana'a, right?" she said before eating her last bite of falafel and disappearing into the kitchen. I breathed a sigh of relief. At least he was alive, crazy, but still alive. Now that I knew he was okay, I decided it would be better if we stayed away from him for a bit.

"By the way," Anna yelled from the kitchen. "I told him we will go to Club Istanbul tomorrow and he should join us!"

A big NO!!! with exclamation marks appeared in my mind, but I knew it was already too late. Invitation delivered. *Politesse avant du tout,* as the Killer would say. Anyways, he had a big imagination, and I consoled myself with the idea that maybe his whole story was made-up or simply part of some paranoid delusion. "Sounds fun," I called back in my most convincing voice.

Things in Yemen were getting bad. A couple of the Austrian Ambassador's bodyguards had been shot a few weeks earlier and an Italian NGO worker had only recently been rescued after a kidnapping. Hanging around a madman in these uncertain times was the last thing I wanted to do, but I didn't want to alarm the other musketeers over nothing. It was better for us to enjoy the night out.

"Thank God It's Thursday!" Anna screamed 24-hours later, turning on dated music. *Everybody dance now!* We got into a dancing mood as we dressed and when we reached Club Istanbul, we hit the dancefloor like pros, we drank like pros, and we partied like pros. Even as we laughed and moved to the music, I couldn't help but steal nervous glances at our male musketeer. I knew how much damage alcohol could do to his mind, how fast his thoughts could flip to old memories or imagined nightmares.

The last song played and the lights came on. The party was over so we piled into the Killer's car, dropping Sarah off at her house and then heading for home. When we turned up our block we noticed there wasn't a single light on in the street.

"The electricity must be off in the entire neighborhood," I said.

Instead of the typical sound of generators buzzing, all we heard were wild dogs howling.

"Are they getting closer?" Anna asked.

"They are," I said. The closer we got to the house, the louder the howls became. As we pulled up to our house, two large wild dogs snarled and jumped at the car. The two dogs became eight, and then twelve, and then a pack of almost twenty-five began attacking. It seemed that their base of operation for the night was just inside the gates of our building.

The Killer tried to pull closer to the doorway, but they continued to circle and snarl and lunge at the car. It was impossible to get out of the car. Wild dogs in Sana'a are known to attack, they can kill, and that night, it seemed that we were the only available prey. We circled the block twice, but it was no use, the pack of savage dogs were an impenetrable wall between us and the front door.

"*Mesdames*, really, if you want, you can sleep in my house," the Killer offered. "*C'est pas un problem.*"

No way, I thought. We are not going to spend the night in the house of a potential killer or in the house of a potential psychopath for that matter.

"Maybe," Anna said.

"I don't know..." I said. Anna looked at me, seeming to say: *Why are you so reluctant about the idea? Is there something wrong?* "Maybe we can try once more from the side street," I said. "A last try". While he circled the block, I tried to call Sarah. She did not answer. I imagined her deeply sleeping. It would be no use to show up at her house, especially since she didn't have a doorbell to ring.

"Everything is closed at this time," the Killer said. "Either we wait in the car for a few hours and then go for tea, or you girls sleep at my apartment. I don't see any other option."

"We will stay at your place," Anna said.

We arrived at The Killer's house and he led us to his bedroom. "You can sleep here and I will stay on the couch," he said.

"Thanks, you are very kind," I muttered.

When he left, Anna and I laid next to each other on his big bed. I debated telling her about our friend's past, but I didn't want to scare her. Besides, we were already inside his house. After five minutes I could hear her deep breathing as she slept.

I tried to stay awake on a surveillance mission. I watched the window overlooking a corridor that led to the living room where the Killer slept. I wondered what would happen if he got angry for some imagined betrayal or paranoid affront. And what if his story was true? I wondered if someone would come here and attack us in the night, the way he had attacked so many others. I was relieved to hear birds beginning to sing outside. It felt safer with the sun rising. In my relief, I drifted off into a sudden and deep sleep.

A few hours later, I opened a lazy eye and jumped. The Killer was quietly sitting at the edge of the bed watching me. I pulled the sheet to my neck and sat up. "Where is Anna?"

CHAPTER 23

"Come on, my lazy princess!" he grinned at me. "I can see you slept well in my bed, it is almost 9:30."

"And Anna?" I got worried. No answer.

"Where is Anna?" I repeated.

"She got up early and I drove her home. She didn't want to wake you, but she wanted to have breakfast in your house and thought you might like to have breakfast somewhere outside with me."

He moved closer and I sprang out of bed, still dressed in my party clothes. "No, I think I should go home, too," I said.

"Okay, but you have to accept coffee first. I will prepare some, my princess," he said, leaving the bedroom whistling an old bolero song.

Shit! I thought. It didn't matter if he was actually a killer on the run from other killers or a paranoid madman, all I knew was that I needed to get out of his house as quickly as possible. I pulled on my shoes, combed my hair, and covered myself under layers of Zorro mask, and Batman cape. The black layers had become a standard requirement for foreign women who wanted to step into the street. I walked into the living room, hoping to slip out the front door. Then I realized that I didn't have my handbag. I rushed back to the bedroom. It was nowhere in sight. I wondered if Anna had taken it with her, but she had her own keys...

"My princess," he called from the kitchen. "Coffee is ready!"

I returned to the living room and spotted my handbag in the corner behind the Killer, who had taken a seat on the couch with two little cups of black espresso sitting on the table before him. *Espresso, so tempting!* I thought. My handbag was within reach. I could have grabbed it and shouted an excuse on my way out the door. Instead, I looked back and forth from the coffee to The Killer and then took a seat next to him.

He was looking for something on his phone and when he looked up, a slow melody started playing. It was an old Cuban love song, the same bolero he had been whistling before. *En las sensuales líneas de tu cuerpo hermoso, las curvas que se admiran despiertan ilusión....*

"Would you like to go to Cuba?" he asked.

"Of course, who wouldn't like to?" I said, shrugging. The music played on, *y es la cadencia de tu voz tan cristalina, tan suave y argentada...*

"I will tell you a secret, but please don't tell anyone," he said, looking down into his coffee. *que impresionada por todos tus encantos...*

"I promise," said, knowing I would have said anything he wanted to ensure an easy departure from his home. I was in survival mode.

"I will escape to Cuba," he said, closing his eyes and swaying to the music. *Por ese cuerpo orlado de belleza...*

"Escape?" I asked incredulously. *Tus ojos soñadores y tu rostro angelical...*

"They found me, they know where I am and soon they will come. They could come at any time..."

"To make you work again for them?" I asked, playing his game.

"I cannot do that anymore," he said calmly, taking a sip of his coffee and humming. *Te comparo con una santa diosa!*" I just want a calm life. My optometrist clinic and a wife and a family I can hug when I arrive home. Do you know my princess, I respect you a lot?"

He turned to look at me, taking my hands in his and staring at me for a long time. *Longina seductora cual flor primaveral...*

I could see it coming. He took a deep breath and asked. "My princess, will you come with me?"

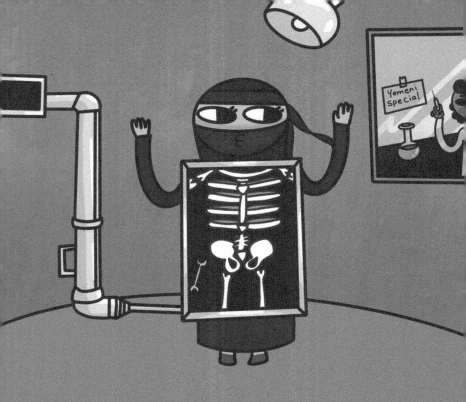

THE
Butcher
Hospital

One day I got very sick. I had been feverish and taking medication for two weeks, but my health was not improving. I called my Yemeni friend who works for a pharmaceutical company in hopes that he could help.

Later that day, he passed by my house with his friend, an old doctor. The guy didn't look very neat and trim, but in my sick state I had no energy to complain. He too was wary of the visit, agreeing to see me only after a lot of convincing arguments from my friend who insisted that it was okay for him to see me, even without my father or non-existent husband present.

As the doctor examined me, he began complaining to my friend about the recurrent and long-standing lack of anesthesia in Yemeni hospitals. He casually mentioned that doctors now used cocaine in place of anesthesia during operations. He was amused by the use of this old Soviet trick, which doctors his age who had studied in the URSS during the sixties had long known about.

I wanted to scream, but instead I just stared at them in horror, thinking: *Hello doctor! I am in front of you and I don't want to hear about the current lack of anesthesia in the country that I'm now sick in!*

He finished his exam and the verdict was...no verdict. He didn't know what I had, but since I had already been taking medicine for two weeks, he decided it was time for the Yemen's special. He put together a Molotov cocktail of antihistamine, antibiotic, antiallergy, and, the cherry on the top, cortisone, all to be administered in two jabs, each syringe containing enough medication to kill a horse.

I don't trust Yemeni doctors, and I was even more skeptical of one who would prescribe me an injection of every medication available on the market. Fortunately, I am a female, and it proved too much for the good doctor to see an unaccompanied female butt, even if only to jab it twice with a needle. I was suddenly grateful for gender segregation.

He hurried out of the house leaving behind a bunch of little pots with liquid inside that I was supposed to get injected somewhere, by someone, somehow. As reluctant as I was to take the injection, I was more afraid of ending up in a Yemeni hospital, so I called Anna.

I hoped she would be able to give me the injection since she had been working in a hospital (in administration, but still in a hospital). She arrived home and after I showed her some YouTube videos on how to inject the cocktail in the upper quarter of my butty, she categorically refused.

When Anna refuses, there's no way you will change her mind. No means no. She offered me an alternative. She knew a small clinic run by a Syrian and an Iraqi doctor. I trust Syrian doctors, and though I had not yet had the chance to be treated by an Iraqi doctor, it sounded like my best option. Anyone but Yemeni doctors, about whom I'd heard far too many stories about people getting the wrong leg cut off or being injected with horse medicine.

I got dressed and she dragged me to the clinic. Fortunately, it was very close, since she had to carry my weight as I limped along beside her. The Syrian doctor checked the medicines I brought him and decided to inject three of them. After getting three shots, I went home and slept for a peaceful 12-hours. He had mentioned this would happen, so I found it normal. What was not normal was the fever that raged on even after playing Sleeping Beauty for half a day. There was no avoiding it. The time had come for me to face one of my worst nightmares and go to a hospital in Yemen.

I brought my 100% tribal-looking Yemeni friend with me. The crowds of people and echoing screams made me feel like I was at a weekly street market or a zoo. There was no reception, no queue, only people shouting in the corridors and grabbing doctors and nurses as they passed by. An old lady was making a big show next to me, screaming and insanely pulling on her clothes. Children ran up and down the corridor where I was sitting and some men leaned on their Kalashnikovs chewing qat.

My friend made me sit in a chair while he literally tackled a doctor on his way somewhere else. When he dragged the doctor over to check on me, I was in such a haze that he had to pull me by the Batman cape to the x-ray room. They left me fully clothed as they scanned me. This resulted in the most hilarious x-ray of my lungs in which you can hardly see them at all. What is clear in the x-ray, are the two metal clasps of my bra, the pins holding my niqab in place, and the bling decorating the edges of my abbaya. This made my doctor back home break into inappropriate laughter when she reviewed them months later.

After my x-ray, it was time for a blood test, taken directly from the vein with a huge needle that I was sure I'd seen in the hands of farm veterinarians. When we returned the next day for the results, the doctor looked down at his report and sighed. "Sorry, we don't know what you have, but I can give you an injection of the Yemen's special."

No way I was getting that cocktail again, my body would implode. I decided not to take anything and just lay half-dead in my bed. It took a long two-weeks to start feeling better, almost a month to fully function again, but I survived with or the Yemen's special.

CHAPTER 24

"He has a gun," Anna said the moment I walked into the flat.

"What?" I exclaimed.

"He has a gun," she shrieked, clearly upset.

"I've heard this already..." I snapped, knowing who she must be talking about. "Where did you see him?"

"His eyes are full of blood and anger..." she said, pacing.

"Anna, where? Where did you see him?"

"The café, our café," she said.

I ran out the door and found a taxi. As we drove, I began to realize that I was making a stupid decision. Everyone needs to make stupid decisions sometimes, I reasoned. My life would be boring without making them from time to time. The truth was, I cared about The Killer. He might have done terrible things in the past, he might not have, but who was I to judge him? All I knew for sure was that he needed help, and I thought that maybe I could prevent him from doing something stupid.

When I arrived, I didn't seem him. I called, but he didn't pick up. I tried again but nothing. I rushed to the second floor, to our usual table, but he was nowhere to be seen. I hurried back to the first floor, which was crowded with groups of men. I scanned their faces until I spotted one of his medical student friends drinking tea and smoking shisha. I walked over and told him to call me right away if he saw the Killer. I hurried to write down my number on the first napkin I found, the edges stained with tea. As I handed it to him, I noticed curious eyes and dirty smiles at the surrounding tables.

I retreated to the second floor and sat down at our table to call him again. This time, it didn't even ring. His phone was turned off. "What did you do?" I whispered. The waiter appeared with a big pot of hot water and a bag of green tea that I hadn't ordered. My usual. My nerves were raw as I sipped my tea, every sound made me jump. I stared at the screen of my phone, willing it to ring. Then I heard a loud crash downstairs as if a whirlwind had entered the café. His voice boomed, too loudly, followed by the softer voices of his friend and our waiter.

I ran towards the stairs and heard the sound of glasses clinking together and a table being pushed across the floor. Then I heard my name, and footsteps on the stairs. We came face-to-face in the middle of the staircase. Before I could say a word, he took my arm with such force that before I knew what was happening, I was back in my usual seat at our usual table, my green tea sitting cold on the table.

"You are here my princess! I am so happy to see your face, maybe for the last time," he said, looking around nervously. He shifted in his seat, standing up and sitting back down. Though he smelled like tea, no doubt taken from his friend's table moments earlier, I could tell he was drunk.

"Today I will solve everything, don't worry," he said, as he stood up and sat down again. I spotted the handle of his gun tucked between his jeans and black leather belt. I didn't know anything about handguns, just that this one was big. "Then I will disappear for a while. Or I will be dead. It is my only chance."

I glanced over and saw that his friend had followed him upstairs and was standing in the stairway. He seemed unsure whether to get closer or stay back. I made a small gesture with my hand to tell him to stay where he was.

"Why are you carrying a gun?" I asked as calmly as I could.

"Because they are here, I told you," he said, leaning forward. "Today it will all get decided. And God willing I will be the one who survives."

"You are very upset, you cannot go anywhere like that. Stay here with me for a while, please," I said, taking his hand.

"Did you think about what I asked you?"

"Cuba?"

"Shhh..." he hissed, looking over his shoulder. "Don't say it so loud."

I stared at him, sad and afraid for my friend. I didn't know what to say to calm him down or to keep things from getting worse.

"I need to go," he stood up. "If you don't see me anymore it is probably because I am dead."

"Wait, don't..." I started to say.

"If I survive, I will come to your house before disappearing from here, okay?" he kissed my hand. "Pray for me my princess," he called, as he ran down the stairs. Thankfully, his friend was no longer there.

I waited for two hours, drinking my cold green tea. I called and called, but his phone remained switched off. Finally, I headed back home.

CHAPTER 25

At almost 11 p.m., there was still no news from him or from any of his acquittances. Anna wasn't home and I felt like the walls were caving in. I was really worried about what he could do to others, or to himself.

I picked up my little wooden cross, playing with it. Finally, I decided to go downstairs to the shop on the corner of my street to get some fresh air and clear my mind. I kissed the little cross for His blessings and set it on the side table near the couch.

At the shop I picked up things automatically, grabbing some yoghurt and bread and other things I didn't remember taking. I walked upstairs with the bag of groceries I didn't need. At my door, I reached in my bag to find my keys. Then the lights in the stairwell went out. They always switched off automatically after a few minutes, I considered turning them back on, but then I felt the shape of the key. I grabbed it and felt for the lock, sliding in my key and turning the knob to the left.

Before I knew what was happening, I felt someone push me into the house from behind. The door slammed shut behind us. I knew it was a man, because he was big and strong enough to push me towards the living room despite my attempts to turn and squirm away. I felt something cold between me and him. I wondered if it was a gun. Suddenly, the pressure of his arms around my body slackened and I turned towards him. I lunged forward and hugged him.

I was surprised by my reaction. I wondered who in their right mind hugs someone pointing a gun at them? But it was my friend, The Killer. I stepped back and felt a chill. My first reaction at seeing him alive had been relief, but that was quickly fading into fear. His eyes looked vacant and wild with paranoia. He rushed past me, his gun drawn as he checked every room in the house. When he returned to the kitchen, he went to the cupboard where the alcohol was kept, filling two glasses with vodka and taking a seat on the couch.

I stood in the middle of the living room watching him.

"Come here, come on," he said, waving me toward the couch. "Drink with me like we always do." I silently walked towards him, as if in a trance, and took a seat. "It is time for me to disappear, my princess. But don't worry, I am not abandoning you here, I will always keep an eye on you, to make sure you are safe."

"What happened when you left the café?" I asked, my heart beating faster in my chest.

"I couldn't find them, but I need to go," he said. "My princess, please, come with me."

"No, I cannot do that," I said.

"I will not touch you, I promise, until you are ready," he pleaded. "Then, we will create a family, we will be happy..."

"I don't want that," I said, cutting him off.

"This is the plan, now it would be too dangerous to leave together. I will leave for a few months, maybe to Bahrain, maybe to Oman. And in two or three months, when I make sure they cannot track me, I will go to Cuba," he continued, not hearing a word I said. "You will join me there, right my princess?"

"No, I will not," I said, involuntarily taking the cross from the table and passing it through my fingers.

"Whenever you feel ready, I will send you the tickets to La Habana, in your name," he rambled on. "I will be waiting for you there. We will start our life together there."

"That will never happen," I said, knowing that I was speaking only to myself.

He took an envelope and placed it in my hands. "Memorize it and burn it, ok? No one should see this. No one. And remember, if there are any problems before Cuba, contact me and I will be here faster than you can imagine. I am the Air and I will always protect you."

He pushed the envelope deeper into my hands and took my cross from my fingers. "Can I keep it with me?"

"You are not Christian," I said.

"It comes from you. This will protect me. I will always wear it," he said, gripping it tightly. "Give me a last kiss."

He brought his cheek near me and when I leaned forward to kiss it, he turned his head and our lips met. "My princess," he smiled, eyes closed. "À bientôt."

He leapt of the couch and ran out the door. I got up and locked the door behind him, though I knew I wouldn't see him again. I returned to the couch and opened the envelope. I wondered what I would find inside. I unfolded the paper. It was blank.

Adventure 4
Mr. Special Forces

CHAPTER 26

My phone rang and the name ANNA appeared in all capital letters on the screen. "Do you have any plans for tonight?" she asked excitedly. My flatmate's question was rhetorical. She knew that Thursday nights in Yemen had meant zero plans for weeks. Club Istanbul had even shut its doors due to low attendance by their expat customer base. Most were no longer free to roam around as they had before. It had become too dangerous.

"No..." I replied.

"I've just met some people from the German embassy, they are going to the British base for a farewell party," she said, sounding giddy. "Do you want to come?"

"Hmm," I said. As I have already mentioned, Anna has the ability to meet and befriend the most random people in the most random places, from the typical taxi driver who doesn't know a word of English to top ambassadors who barely leave their houses. People who are impossible to meet when you are trying, she just finds them out of the blue. I hesitated, knowing Anna's plans always came with a surprise twist.

"They will have beer there, they told me they even have a bar inside the base, can you believe it?" she added.

"Sure, let's go," I said, my hesitation vanishing. I didn't know the Germans, I didn't know the British, or the host of the party leaving Yemen, and I particularly disliked these military compounds, but a proper bar inside was something of a dream those days in Yemen when the only alcohol we could find was smuggled from Djibouti and came with the risk of blindness. Embassies brought their own, dispatched as diplomatic valise, premium quality. I needed a drink.

A few hours later, Anna, Sarah (after being convinced by Anna through a tougher wearing down process than I'd needed) and I headed onto a military base. We had no idea where exactly the party was being held, nor did we have confirmation from Anna's new friends that we had been added to the guest list, but we assumed that we would be allowed in. Afterall, for a male expat to have three young, non-prostitute girls arrive at an all-male party was about as much of a victory as one could hope for.

I lived outside of the world of embassies, security compounds and UN staff. It was a niche expat community all its own. These people worked together, lived together, partied together, and rarely stepped out of their enclosure to visit the real world. As we drove through the compound, I wondered if I had been intentionally avoiding these people and places, as they were not generally my cup of tea, or if I hadn't made it into one of the compounds because they were out of my reach. Anna was not really into the snobby, toffee-nosed diplomatic environment either, but as the security situation continued to deteriorate in Sana'a, the invitations to these cloistered worlds became more appealing.

I had long argued that they were the biggest targets of all. Since our usual party places had been closed and our favorite caffeine and shisha spots on Hadda street had become less safe, there was less and less for us to do. And if foreigners were the targets, the best places to attack were locations where only foreigners hung out. And a bunch of white middle-age male UN officials make a very succulent bounty. That made attending the party a very stupid move. Anna and I both knew this, but boredom is the greatest motivator.

We eventually found the party and the typical procedure started: Capes off, smile on and...let's grab a beer! That first sip of fresh beer after so many long, dry weeks was refreshing. Anna's new friends hadn't yet arrived, but people, to be more exact, security people, and to be even more exact, male security people, had started to gather around us. We discovered that the British guy who'd first greeted us was the one leaving the country. The Germans appeared and more introductions were made. They were nice, clever guys, but they knew so many people at the party that they were kept busy making the rounds to greet everyone. Sarah didn't move from my side. I could see she was not feeling at ease in these surroundings, and neither was I, so we moved around the room like conjoined twins, while Anna attacked the beer dispenser.

When the bottles of alcohol started to empty, the British hosts revealed the big surprise. They had organized a gymkhana of competitive events and it was time to play. Combine British humor with feats of military physical strength and you will have an idea of the sort of races included in that field day competition. The game was clearly unsuitable for our heels and short dresses, so Sarah and I strategically disappeared from the party hall. For her, it was too many men, too many foreigners, and most of them native English speakers with such thick accents she could barely understand them. We ducked onto a terrace and Sarah lit one of her slim cigarettes.

I'd assumed all the soldiers were in the party hall showing off their virile braveness, so I was startled to see a group of five men sitting on the far side of the terrace. I watched them, assuming they'd only stepped out for a smoke and would head back inside, but none of them were smoking. Upon closer inspection, it seemed that they were feeling as bored and out of place as we were. One of them was trying valiantly to make eye contact with me, and finally I relented. After a few glances and hidden smiles, he got up and walked to our table. I have never been into bodies; for me it does not matter if a guy has a nice body shape or not. If I meet a guy and my friends ask me about him, it takes extra effort to physically describe him, but this man was so big, and in such great shape, even I took notice.

"Hello!" he said confidently.

"You guys are from Spain?" I asked; the man's accent had left no doubt. "I can speak some Spanish, if you'd prefer."

His face brightened and he started talking non-stop in his native tongue. It seemed he and his friends had been asked to the party by their British counterparts, but they didn't know many people and weren't comfortable speaking English. It suddenly made sense why they were as out of place as we were. His colleagues seemed so happy to hear their native language, that they rushed to surround us, asking one question after the other. They were warm and friendly, and I felt more at ease on the terrace than I had inside. Sarah couldn't get a word of what we were saying, but she was enjoying the show as if watching TV, looking at us with amused eyes.

I learned from Mr. Special Forces that he and his friends were all members of a special unit protecting the Spanish Embassy in Sana'a. It was then that I remembered where I had seen one of his friends before. He had been at the housewarming party Mr. Engineer had crashed months before. As we talked, Mr. Special Forces made it clear to his colleagues that he was staking his claim on me. He seemed to believe that since he had discovered me, the *no flirting with my new girl* rule was implied. He leaned close, letting his giant frame create a barrier between his friends and I. Sarah had all the attention of the others, like a princess surrounded by special bodyguards.

The gymkhana finished and we could hear the sounds of the party winding down. The final speech was commencing, so we reluctantly went inside. I covertly texted my usual taxi driver, Saddam. The speech droned on and Saddam texted that he was outside. I scanned the room for Mr. Special Forces, but he seemed to have disappeared. I spotted one of his friends.

"I'll be right out," I whispered to Anna and Sarah, who were already heading for the door.

I hadn't exchanged numbers with Mr. Special Forces, and in an uncharacteristically bold move, I raced across the room and handed my business card to his friend. "Here, you and your friends can call me anytime, if you guys need help with translation or anything," I added lamely.

I got in the taxi and my phone chimed. *Do you have WhatsApp?* It was obvious the SMS came from one of the Spaniards, but which one was not so clear. My phone chimed again. *You can add me in this other number.* I did and I was relieved to see that the profile picture was that of Mr. Special Forces. The business card had reached its correct destination.

Hi. I texted, smiling at the success of my trick and thinking, *Jackpot!* I'd gotten the cute one.

CHAPTER 27

I soon realized my mistake. One innocent little "*Hi!*" had resulted in 15 new Spanish messages in the space of five minutes. I replied after half an hour with a single sentence, which yielded 25 new messages in two minutes time. I replied three hours later with a single syllable. 50 new messages received in 30 seconds!

"Fast hands, you Spaniard," I whispered. "I hope you are not as fast in everything as you are in writing replies..." I went to bed, and when I woke up the next morning, I was terrified to check the number of messages I might have waiting. But there was only one.

Do you want to pass by for dinner tomorrow? We are having a family dinner with my colleagues at our house, next to the embassy.

"Thank, God!" I muttered, thinking that he must have finally gotten the hint that I was not a fan of encyclopedic texting. Spanish food? I wrote back.

Yes, I am cooking.

Cool, I will come with Sarah... you have your bodyguards, so I need to bring mine too! What time and where is your house?

8:30 p.m. I will pick you up in front of La Maison hotel.

I read his message and remembered the standard security rule that most foreign soldiers in Yemen followed of not ever telling anyone their exact location. *Perfect. I'll see you there.*

At 8:35 p.m., I was surprisingly almost on time. I waited with Saddam in front of La Maison hotel. Sarah had already gotten her fill of foreigners the night before, so she'd texted me at the last minute that she couldn't join me. I didn't see the Spaniards, but I told Saddam not to wait and walked into the hotel alone. At 8:40, there was still no news and I began to worry. Security people were supposed to be exact, military time and all that, so maybe they had already come and gone during the five minutes I was late. When Anna's German soldier friends told her that they would arrive in seven minutes, they arrived in literally seven minutes and zero seconds. At 8:50 p.m., I received a text message. *Sorry, we will be a little late, headed towards you now.* A bit late? I wanted to shout. I started typing: *I've already been waiting for 20 minutes...* I deleted the message. I was always late, I couldn't blame them for my most typical shortcoming. They might have been in security, but they were still Spanish. At 9:04 p.m., they texted again: *We are at the door. Grey car.*

I peeked outside. There was no grey car, but I noticed a white armored car. The windows were tinted, but I walked towards it anyways. The door opened and Mr. Special Forces grinned out at me. "Nice white car," I said sarcastically. No one seemed to hear my comment, and before I knew it, I was wedged in the middle seat between two giant soldiers.

Mr. Special Forces was driving, and he seemed to barely fit as he hunched over the wheel. Speeding around the turns, a pistol dug into my left hip, then another poked my right calf. My heart began to race, panic rising in my chest as I realized that being in the car with special security soldiers was as good as driving around Sana'a with a target on my chest. We pulled up to a gated house and I heard the crackle of a walkie-talkie. *"Recibido,"* replied the metallic voice of the walkie. The gate opened.

CHAPTER 28

The house was small, and I learned that it had previously been used by one of the Spanish diplomats, but occasionally, since the diplomat had relocated to the embassy for security reasons, the security guys would hang out in the house on their free evenings. We entered and the guys took off their guns and I removed my black cape. A very nice smell was coming from the kitchen where Mr. Special Forces had already started cooking. *Rioja* wine was poured and we chatted about this and that, our conversation animated from the moment we raised our glasses. The soldiers were being goofy, talking loudly, and laughing without a hint of the seriousness they'd had during our drive. For a moment, I felt perfectly at home. With the food came more wine, and one of the soldiers began to sing an opera song as Mr. Special Forces served dessert: home-made Crema Catalana, a sort of crème brulee with a burnt sugar crust, followed by real coffee and shots of hazelnut liqueur.

When it was time to go home, Mr. Special Forces offered to drive me. I watched him, trying to determine how drunk he was. He seemed fine and I wondered how much wine it would take to get a man his sized tipsy. Anyhow, it seemed safer to ride in an armored car with him than to walk on the street and take a random taxi. I said goodbye to everyone with a couple of kisses on the cheek while he collected his guns. To my surprise, only the two of us walked towards the car.

"Don't you security boys have to drive around in pairs, like hubby and wife?" I teased him, knowing that they weren't allowed to drive alone.

"If he is the boss, hubby can keep his wives at home. And you are driving with the *jefe*."

"Watch out, when you come back the wives might not open the door," I teased him.

He started the engine and the doors opened. "Where is your home?" he asked.

"Very close to here, just take Road 27 to the third street, then left at the intersection of 8th Street."

I was surprised to see him turn on the car's GPS. Our neighborhood was built much later than the rest of the city, which meant that it was one of the few in Sana'a that has planned, straight streets, street names, and house numbers. My previous neighborhood in the old city had felt like a maze by comparison. It had taken me no less than three weeks until I could avoid getting lost on my way home, and months more to get to know it well. As things became more dangerous, my organization had offered me a house in the new part of the city, in a "good area", where it was basically impossible to get lost.

As I looked out the window, I started to feel like we were going completely in the opposite direction of my neighborhood, but surely his military GPS system couldn't be wrong. "I can give you directions, if you like," I shyly suggested.

"Thanks, but I know the way," he said, looking at me with a big, patronizing smile.

"Okay," I said, wondering how tipsy I must be to feel lost this close to my home. It was this man's job to drive the Ambassador and diplomats safely through the city, so he must have known a shortcut. Then I spotted the banners hanging over the street, emblazoned with anti-Western slogans. Alarm bells went off in my head. "Wait, stop," I shouted. "Do not enter this neighborhood, turn back…"

"What, why? How do you know?" he said, startled by the panic in my voice.

"Didn't you see the banners?"

"I cannot understand them…"

BOWLING
IN
Abbaya

I am bad at sports. All sorts of sports, even chess. I lack basic coordination in general, so add a Batman cape and the results are really disastrous. This doesn't come up often in Yemen, as not many sports are available for females to enjoy.

There is one female-only gym located on the top floor of a posh beauty salon. There you'll find a few fitness machines, but the intensity of talking in that little room is always far higher than the intensity of the workouts. Add to that the fact that there are honey sweets available for post-workout recovery, and chances are you'll end up leaving the gym weighing more than when you arrived.

One exception is bowling. Located in the middle of nowhere in Sana'a, there is a bowling center with eight wide lanes. Families and groups of teenagers go there to have fun and surprisingly, despite some lanes reserved for ladies-only, the space is open and shared and everyone can see each other. This is as amazing as it is counterproductive, because as a lady, these conditions mean you cannot remove your Batman cape while bowling. If a woman was to remove their abbaya, everyone would see and the match would likely end with someone in prison after having been accused of public scandal.

Yemeni girls are so used to wearing the abbaya that it's like a second skin for them, so this poses less of an issue for them. I might have gotten comfortable wearing mine in my daily life, but bowling in abbaya is locals-only-level expertise. Top it off with my poor coordination and it is recipe for mayhem.

One evening, two Yemeni friends and I arrived at the bowling center. We rented our flat bowling shoes and I was pleased to remember that I had an extra pair of socks in my bag. We headed to our lane and added our names to the screen counting our points. My friend put his name and his other friend's name in the counter. Then, in order to keep my anonymity — to reveal the name of a lady in Yemen would be a great attack to her honor — he typed: Yemeni girl. This was especially paradoxical considering that everyone knew from the moment we entered that I was a foreigner.

The guys started the game. Five pins down. Four pins down. I selected a pink ball, the lightest one at eight kilos, and I put my fingers in the holes. I used my other hand to pull the end of my Batman cape up to my knee to accommodate greater movement. I certainly didn't want to fall down and slide down the lane with the ball.

I took a breath and heaved the ball. It rolled, and rolled, and rolled. Instead of going straight, my ball looked as if it was slaloming in a ski lane, first left, now right, now left again till it fell in one of the gutters. Zero pins down. I was given a second chance. Again, Batman cape up. Three steps running towards the lane and... 1 pin falls! Yeheee! My friends applaud my poor success, but I knew my luck was changing! What happened next was completely unexpected by everyone. In the third round, did I get a full strike or did I roll down the lane with my full body and Batman cape? Alea iacta est !*

To this day, I can still feel my body first flying in the sky, floating in the air for microseconds, before obstreperously falling in the lane and rolling what felt like meters. The pins did fall, all of them. And all it cost me was my pride and some monumental bruises.

---

*   The die is cast!

171

CHAPTER 29

"Well, I do, and they mean we should turn back right now," I said. He didn't answer. "I am serious. We shouldn't be here..."

"What is all this fuss for some little bedsheets hanging here and there, it's nice decoration," he added, still not getting it.

I stared at him in shock. I could forgive him for getting lost, but the fact that he could not recognize some pretty obvious slogans from a particular non-Western-friendly group was inexcusable. "This is no-go territory. You are part of the special forces, you are the boss of the unit protecting the Ambassador, you should know where not to go better than I do! Just turn the second next street on the left, it should take us back to the main road."

"Since when do ladies have such a good orientation?" he joked, convinced he was right. "Let me check the GPS, I am sure this is the correct way"

"I do not care about your high-tech GPS. We are in an armored car at ungodly hours in the worst place we can be, so you better follow my directions like a good soldier follows his commander. Full stop."

Something in my tone made him realize how serious the situation was. "Si, vale, you lead," he said.

"Left, right, straight, left, straight, okay, second right. Here, the pink house..." and with a few clear directions, I was safely back home. "Can you get back to the embassy from here?" I asked, quite sure he could not.

"Yes, no problem."

"We can go back together. I can show you the fastest way, so you know for another time..." I offered. As angry as I was at his arrogance, I didn't want him to be killed or kidnapped just because he gave me a ride back home.

"No need, really. I recognize the area. I never get lost," he said so confidently that I couldn't help but laugh.

"Okay, thanks very much for the evening. I really enjoyed it. You and the guys are lovely."

All his confidence while driving had now faded. He looked up at me shyly. "Do you want to see me again, another time?" He asked.

"I'll call you," I replied. I'd had a lovely evening. It was nice company, lots of laughs, an atmosphere of camaraderie, all topped off with amazing food and Rioja. It was definitely enough to make me forget that he'd gotten us lost in a bad neighborhood in a very easy-to-target car, but was it enough to convince me to see him again? The fit-body first impression was gone, I was not sure there was anything else there to keep my interest. It was a question for another day.

CHAPTER 30

Hola! How are you today? Can we pass by for coffee? The latest message from Mr. Special Forces after 35 unanswered ones, was well timed.

Sure, I'm free. I typed back.

Ok, we will come at 7pm.

Do you remember how to reach my house?

Of course.

At 7:25, another message: *We are leaving now, see you in 5 minutes.* Five minutes later my phone rang. "So, listen..." he said. "We are on 10th Street. Can you give us directions from there?"

I didn't know whether to laugh or to cry. It was the third or fourth time the Spaniards had come to my house. "How can you soldiers always be lost?" I asked, giving them directions. Some minutes later they arrived and Mr. Special Forces headed straight for the kitchen to prepare coffee for us. Since their very first visit, they'd behaved as if my home was theirs. This pleased me, it was a sign they had become part of my inner-circle and we were just comfortable hanging out together.

I sat contentedly chatting with Mr. Musculator, Mr. Special Forces' best buddy, and he brought us steaming cups of good, strong espresso. I offered them some cookies, which they declined. Something about an athlete's diet. I watched them laughing conspiratorially as they finish their coffees in a single gulp.

"What is the rush," I asked lightly, knowing it would be hours before their colleagues returned to pick them up.

"You'll see," Mr. Special Forces winked, hurrying to the kitchen and returning with three glasses. He set them on the table and opened his backpack, removing a gun. "Hey," I almost yelled. "Be careful with that thing in my house."

"I'm sorry," he muttered, still digging in his bag.

I began to worry about what else was lurking inside his bag.

"Surprise!" he shouted triumphantly, pulling out a bottle of honey rum.

"Oh my God! Where did you find this?" I asked, grinning from ear to ear. It had been ages since I'd seen an entire bottle of anything with its original seal intact. Instead of answering me, he cracked it open and poured three glasses. *"Salut! Cheers!"*

"Such an exquisite rum," I said a glass and a half later. "Guys, really, where did you find this? I can list at least five embassies that I know of that have no alcohol at all at this moment, and none of my usual smugglers have a drop of it."

They both laughed nervously.

"Sometimes you have to ask firmly to get what you want," Mr. Special Forces said.

"Let's just say we knew a guy in the Spanish embassy who had this bottle," Mr. Musculator held it up. "And mi amigo here gave him *an offer he couldn't refuse.*"

I felt like I was in a Spanish version of the Godfather, a thug on either side of me. "Did you threaten him?" I asked, incredulous.

"I didn't point a gun at him," Mr. Special Forces shrugged.

"Yeah, he just put it on the table and showed him his fist," Mr. Musculator said, breaking into a fit of laughter.

What. The. Fuck. I thought, taking another sip.

"Okay, time to train," Mr. Special Forces said, standing up.

The two giants had decided I needed to learn self-defense for my own good and Mr. Special Forces was theoretically teaching me. Practically, as clumsy as I am, it was just me falling to the floor and him lifting me to my feet again, more of a martial hugs game than a martial arts session.

I fell to the floor, and while graciously doing so thanks to my extensive practice falling everywhere from the street to the middle of the office, I noticed a tattoo on the Special Forces' right ankle.

"Is that a cartoon bee?" I laughed.

He sat up, pulling up the leg of his pants to give me a better look. "Yes, do you like it?"

"It's very funny," I said. Especially on a two-meter-tall giant, I thought. "Why a bee?"

"Because I fly around fast and I sting hard," he winked.

"Do you have more?"

"Yes, I will show you," he said, unbuttoning his khaki shirt.

"No, it's okay," I hurried to add. "I just think a wolf tattoo would have suited you very well."

"Why do you say that?" he asked, suddenly serious.

"I don't know," I shrugged. "Just this look you get sometimes makes you look like one."

"I do have a wolf tattoo," he said pulling up his shirt to reveal a wolf's head positioned on one hip.

"Wow, some guess," I said. "Why did you get this design?"

"Because I am very obsessive. When I start something, I cannot stop. Like a wolf devouring its prey."

"In what way?"

"Any. All. With work, with fights, with women. With drugs especially. That's why I cannot smoke a cigarette, because I will become addicted."

"You are exaggerating."

"No, I am not. I know myself. When I was younger, before entering the army, I used to have a real problem with drugs. Not as much as him, but almost," he said, nodding in Mr. Musculator's direction.

During one of our gatherings over some good paella, Mr. Musculator had told us about growing up in a poor region in southern Spain. He came from a neighborhood riddled with drugs and he and his friends became addicts by the time they were 14. Then his elder brother had died from an overdose. He rethought his life and joined the national police, rising through the ranks in an anti-trafficking unit. "I was so good at it," he'd explained. "Because I knew all the hiding places and tricks from my own experience. I just had to think what I would have done in the same situations." He'd poured a glass of wine before continuing. "Now, most of my old friends are either dead or in prison. When I go home, people don't talk to me. They are scared I want to nick them. But joining the police and then the army was the best decision I made in my life. It kept me away from drugs, from prison, and from problems. I'm good at what I do. I don't need more." If I'd read his story, or seen it on television, I would have found it cliché, but sitting across from someone who had changed his life in such a dramatic way was inspiring.

"But now you are clean, right?" I asked Mr. Special Forces. "I mean, this is not happening so much to you now, these obsessive behaviors?"

"No. Not with drugs," he said. I thought about his frantic calls and messages and the way that the more he drank, the more he resembled an anxious dog. "Enough about that," he pulled down his shirt. "If you had a tattoo, I know what it would be."

"Oh? What's that?"

"A little witch," he grinned. "What we call a *brujita*."

"Really? Why?" I asked, my curiosity peaked.

"Because you bewitched me, and now, I cannot get you out of my mind."

THE DAY

My Oven Exploded

The day my oven exploded, I was still living in this marvelous neighborhood in old Sana'a. It was a neighborhood where magic and reality mixed together. The house itself was a four-floor mud building with labyrinthine stairs and uneven ceilings. Each floor was home to a small, one-bedroom apartment with a shared kitchen on the top floor.

You might think the kitchen was on the top floor to ensure you got plenty of exercise going up and down every time you wanted to have a bite, but the traditional layout, which can be found in most houses in old Sana'a served a different purpose. The kitchen was the place where women spent much of their time and being on the top floor enabled them to spy down the streets without being seen themselves.

On the day in question, I arrived home and after putting on my sweatpants, I headed up to fourth floor to cook some lunch. Everything is at least a millennium old in old Sana'a, and our kitchen was no exception. In one corner, there was an oven with iron plates on which bread could be cooked over wood. It even had two built-in storage bins for grain. The gas cooker was not quite as old as the bread oven. These days, almost all houses in Yemen have gas cookers. Each week, you'll hear the little van rumbling down the street delivering gas. People rush out of their houses screaming at the van (lest it drive away), to secure a full tank to replace their empty ones. Thanks to poor tank maintenance or the occasional faulty pipe, sometimes houses, and the people in them, blow up.

That particular day, I wanted to be healthy. I planned to make a ratatouille of eggplant, zucchini, onion, and pumpkin. I set the ingredients on the table, grabbed a cutting board and a big knife, and started cutting. I stopped slicing after the second eggplant and went over to light the cooker. Crick...Crick...crick. I heard the sound of the lighter click and gas whooshed from the tank through the pipes. I closed the oven door and sat back down to finish cutting my vegetables. Just as I positioned the second eggplant, a fireball exploded out of the oven. I watched across the table in horror as fire spread through the kitchen, though, miraculously, the kitchen didn't take fire, though the walls blackened. I rushed to turn off the oven, shifting the gas pipe to the off position, and ran out of the room.

On my way down the stairs, I ran into my third-floor neighbor. He'd opened the wooden door of his apartment and asked about the explosion. Instinctively, I threw my arms around him in a hug and started crying like a kid, gasping and explaining what had happened between sobs. He stood, giving me a weirdly square, robotic hug. An introvert by nature, he clearly did not know what to do or what to say.

Slowly, I started to calm down. I wiped my eyes and joked about the irony of dying in Yemen while trying to cook a healthy meal. My neighbor did not find this amusing. The calmer I became, the more he freaked out. "It exploded, we were inside, we could have blown up, oh my goodness..." he said, starting to shake from fright the way I had been minutes earlier.

I tried to calm him down using the same arguments he had given me moments earlier, but in the end, we were both too frightened to venture back to the kitchen, so we went back to our respective apartments agreeing to live on egg, cheese and honey sandwiches that required no cooking till the owner came to check the oven.

The owner finally came and my neighbor and I watched vigilantly from the other edge of the kitchen.

"It must have just been an air bubble in the gas tank, *hajja bassita,*" he said casually. "Don't worry, if it had to explode, it would have done so already."

"Wait, but you aren't going to change it? At least the gas tank?" I asked.

"Well, the probability of two air bubbles in one tank are little, so you better keep this one," he said, turning and walking out the door as unbothered as he had arrived.

CHAPTER 31

"Yeehee," I jumped up, waving my phone in my hand. I'd just gotten a text message saying that Club Istanbul would reopen again for the night. "Let's go dance!"

Mr. Special Forces, Mr. Musculator, and Anna looked up from the bottle of vodka we had been drinking. Anna had inherited it as a farewell gift from friends when the embassies they were working in had been closed. "You are crazy, it's raining bombs," said Mr. Special Forces.

"Is there a club in Sana'a? Really?" Mr. Musculator asked hopefully.

"Hell, yes," I said. "Yallah, let's go!" I gave Anna a pleading look.

"I don't think we are authorized to go," Mr. Special Forces added, pouring another shot.

"It's in a compound that only foreigners can enter," I argued. "Don't worry, I will be your bodyguard."

"Come on guys, let's go," Anna jumped in.

"Alright, the girls are going," I smiled. "Boys, you are welcome to join. Up to you!"

"Other men will be around?" Mr. Special Forces said, looking up.

"It's a club."

"We are going, too," he said, standing.

Promising to be back in a few hours with a new bottle of whatever they could find, the guys left to go change.

Military uniforms and weapons were not the best choice of clubbing attire. Anna and I weren't convinced they would be back, but it didn't matter, we were in a party mood. We were dancing in our living room to the sound of an obscure Russian punk band that Anna loved when the doorbell rang.

"*Hola!* We are here!" I heard Mr. Special Forces call out.

I couldn't believe they'd found the house on their own. I opened the door and tried not to stare. It was the first time I'd seen him without a uniform on, and his street clothes accentuated the curves of his strong body. He was carrying a half-empty bottle of vodka, which I took from him, pouring a couple of glasses for me and Anna. When the Spaniards began showing off their hot Latino moves, somehow keeping time with the rhythm Russian punk rock, I knew we were in for a good night.

Our soldiers left to perform their usual ceremony of checking the car -on one side, the other side, then under the wheels. Once they'd established that no bombs had been planted in or on the car while we were inside drinking, they signaled for us to come out. We drunkenly piled in the car and I began giving directions. Anna started knocking on the bulletproof glass that separated us from the back end of the car. Two knocks. Two knocks more. "There is a cat in the trunk," she said in a sing-song voice.

I ignored her and tried to concentrate on giving directions.

"Can we take him into the Club with us?" she giggled.

"Who?" I turned and came face-to-face with a fluffy Angora cat, staring at me from behind the bullet-proof glass. "Oh my God," I jumped.

"What?" shouted Mr. Special Forces from the front seat.

"There really is a cat in the trunk!" I laughed. "Why would you guys bring a cat to party with us?"

Mr. Musculator turned to look. "*La puta!*" he shouted. "That's the Ambassador's cat!"

Mr. Special Forces slammed on the brakes and turned around. "Oh, fuck," he said.

"Is your real mission in Yemen to protect the Ambassador's cat?" Anna said, laughing hysterically.

"It's his favorite cat," he said, looking worried. "It must have entered the car when we went to change clothes."

"Wait, wait, wait," I said, choking back laughter. "So, you guys checked the car for bombs twice, but didn't see there was a cat inside?"

"If the Ambassador realizes it is not at his residence, he will go crazy," he said, ignoring me. "We need to go back."

"No way! We are very close to the club and if we wait any longer to enter, we will face problems at the gate," I said. "I will not ruin my party night because an Angora cat needs to get home to the Ambassador."

The boys looked at one another.

"The Ambassador probably does not yet realize the cat's gone," said Mr. Musculator. "We can leave the window open a little so the cat can be comfortable while we dance."

"Yes, and then you two and your cat can all go back home together," I grinned.

When we entered the club, all eyes were on us. The DJ changed the Lebanese song to Shakira's *Loca!* and we all started dancing. Having a partner who knew how to move was a welcome change, and for the first hour we didn't stop to sit or drink. I danced closer and closer to Mr. Special Forces, too close for Yemeni standards, but acceptable inside a club. I placed my hand on his hip and felt something hard.

"Did you bring your gun into the club?" I asked, stepping back.

"Of course," he said. "The bodyguard at the entrance didn't have a clue." He laughed a silly, childish laugh.

"Okay, time for a break," I said. I left the dance floor and felt arms wrap around me. "Mama Coco!" I turned to hug her.

"Is he your boyfriend?" she asked.

"Which one?" I winked.

"Any," she grinned.

"Black-hair is all yours," I nodded to Mr. Musculator.

She approached him, shaking her voluptuous hips, and his face paled. He turned and moved towards the bar, but Coco wasn't easy to dodge.

"Don't worry, dancing is free," I whispered in his ear as she cornered him. He nearly climbed over the chairs to escape to the bar as Coco and I fell over laughing.

Mr. Special Forces continued to drink and started to become suffocating. He danced too close, whatever the song playing, techno or salsa, he was all around me like an octopus with eight arms. He was getting on my nerves, but I didn't want to make a scene knowing that he had a gun. The worst was his look, he was devouring me with his eyes.

The music stopped and lights came on, signaling it was time to go home. We got in the car and began to drive towards home. "Aww," Anna said sleepily. "The cat's not here."

"The cat!" I'd totally forgotten about the cat.

"It must be hiding," Mr. Special Forces said. "Maybe near the spare wheel?"

"The window was only open 2-centimeters," Mr. Musculator said. "It has to be in here."

"I don't see it back here," I said. "He must have escaped the same way he got in."

"Fuck," Mr. Special Forces pounded on the steering wheel. "Did we really just lose the Ambassador's cat?"

We rode the rest of the way home in silence. I imagined the cat had gotten bored of his life in the pompous residence. I imagined he wanted to be free to explore the world beyond the compound walls. He was like the rest of us those days in Yemen, craving freedom, dreaming of a different life outside compound walls, and risking too much for a taste of it. Out there, surrounded by ferocious stray cats, the poor furry cat had probably last alive less than two seconds.

CHAPTER 32

Mr. Special Forces and his friends arrived at my door fully covered in weapons like an exaggerated version of a solider one might see in a Rambo movie. I had been expecting them for coffee, but he'd called minutes earlier. "*Brujita*, how are you, *mi amor*?" he said. "Listen, we have a small problem with our plans today."

"Oh, are you too busy to stop by?"

"No, of course not, but instead of being two of us, we are six."

"You know me, the more the merrier," I said.

"Great, *gracias*..."

"See you soon, then?"

"There is also another little problem."

"Okay..."

"We are coming directly from somewhere, and we have a few extra weapons with us, and I know Anna doesn't like weapons in your house."

"I will manage that, just call me before you arrive," I said, looking across the table at Anna and our Yemeni friend, Tarek, who were having coffee. I had to act fast. "Listen, the guys are coming for coffee, maybe we can move to the terrace upstairs since they are six and we don't have much space down here."

"Okay," she shrugged, and the three of us moved onto the terrace. Two minutes later, I heard the guys arrive. I opened the door to six *Rambos* still decked out in helmets, bulletproof vests, military uniforms, boots, two guns, one knife, and a big rifle each. One even carried a big machine gun, that I'd only ever seen attached to the cars. I wondered how and where I could hide that many guns.

I opened the drawer under the couch and they placed most of the equipment and big guns in there. I stashed the little ones and knives in a small box at the entrance of the living room, and just as Tarek and Anna walked down the stairs, I pushed the machine gun inside the fridge.

"The terrace is too cold, let's stay in here," Anna said, as she and Tarek sat down on the couch. I could see Mr. Special Forces and his friends glancing nervously at the drawer beneath them.

The boys hurried to drink their coffee, clearly uncomfortable. Anna looked at me and whispered. "What's wrong with them today?" She stood up. "I'll get them some milk from the fridge, they are too nervous for espresso."

"I'll go," I said jumping from the sofa to the fridge, semi opening the door and grabbing the milk. I looked at the clock. I knew the boys would have to leave soon, but Anna and Tarek were deep in conversation.

"*Brujita*, I'm sorry, but we need to get back," Mr. Special Forces said, standing. The guys began to collect their usual weaponry from the small box at the entrance. Then they stood staring at me.

"Ahem," I cleared my throat and looked at Anna. "Sorry to bother you guys, but can you please stand up for a moment?" The boys hurried over to retrieve their guns, much to the astonishment of Tarek and Anna. "Sorry!" I mouthed to Anna. I took the brick of milk and placed it back to the fridge and got the machine gun out, giving it to the guys, before following them downstairs.

"I hope I didn't get you in trouble," Mr. Special Forces said when we reached the bottom of the stairs.

"It will be fine," I said.

"*Brujita*, I need to ask you something," he said. "Why do we never see each other alone, why do you avoid me?"

"Avoid you?" I laughed. "You called me to invite over five other men, remember?" I said to pass him the ball.

"I want to see you alone. You are always on my mind, you are the blood that runs in my veins..."

"Okay, okay," I stopped him before he could go any further. "Do you want to come over this evening to talk? I know you cannot leave the compound alone, bring one of your friends, that is fine..."

"I will be here. Just me," he said, a smile on his face and a wolf-like look in his eye.

POOL
Of My Own
IN SANA'A

When anyone asked me what I wanted for my birthday, they all got the same answer: A swimming pool. They thought I was joking. A swimming pool in Sana'a? Where to find it and where to put it? But I was not. I was highly serious about it.

The day of my birthday arrived and Anna pulled up in a van with another Yemeni friend of ours. Out came a pool. Not a little plastic swimming pool for kids, but a really fucking awesome huge air structure half pumped up. It was wintertime, so we carried the pool to our *mafraj*, a room present in each and every Yemeni house that is used as a sort of living room with a low sitting couch running around the perimeter, pillows dividing it in individual compartments. It is used for gatherings, but most importantly, as a place to chew qat. It was the perfect place for an indoor swimming pool.

Once inflated, it took up the whole room. Anna and Tareq worked fast, clearly professionals in the art of swimming pool assembly. Meanwhile, I just jumped around the couches like a kid who'd had a sugar rush. When it came time to fill it, Tareq called a water delivery truck. It arrived and we pulled the hose up over the balcony and into the window of the mafraj. Slowly, the pool began to fill. I started texting all my Yemeni crowd: *Swimming pool birthday party tonight! Don't forget your swimsuits!*

When my friends arrive a few hours later, they were hesitant about the swimming pool. Most didn't believe it would actually be there. A few more trusting friends brought their swimsuits. The party started and some sat on the couches chewing qat with their trousers rolled up, feet floating in the water, others plunged in and danced in the water. We painted our faces with body paint for kids. Some of the qat chewers joined the dancers in the water.

The afternoon passed and so did the evening and we were just there, playing like kids and simply having fun. That pool was a magic door to a much-needed, child-like freedom. Like a little girl who wished for a unicorn, my outlandish wish of having a swimming pool in the middle of winter in Sanaa, had come true. I couldn't have been happier. It felt like proof that the impossible might just be possible if you dare to ask.

CHAPTER 33

I could smell men's cologne before I heard the knock on my door. When I opened it, all two meters of Mr. Special Forces leapt forward, carrying me upstairs like a doll and closing the door behind us. He started unbuttoning his shirt, revealing a perfectly chiseled body. I put my hand on his chest to stop him.

"Do you want some coffee?" I asked, moving past him to the kitchen. He was going too far, too fast.

He threw his big arms around me, hugging me strongly from behind so that I couldn't move. He smelled my neck, and I felt him pressing himself into me. He began to caress me and unfastened the first button of my blouse. He turned me around to face him, leaning down for a kiss. My body froze from fear, I wanted to shout but the words were not coming out of my mouth. A startled look came over his face and he looked down. I followed his gaze and saw that the bulge had disappeared from his pants. "This has never happened to me before," he said, backing away.

"Don't worry about it," I said, trying to hide my relief. With his shirt open, I notice two tattoos I hadn't seen before. One was the face of Jesus, and the other appeared to be a cross. "I never saw these tattoos before."

"Yes, Jesus Christ and the cross," he said, buttoning up his shirt.

"Do they protect you?" I asked, to keep the conversation diverted from what it had just happened.

"They remind me of why I am here."

"What do you mean?" I said.

"What we started a long time ago is not finished yet, it will not finish till we defeat those infidels."

"What?" I started to laugh, but then I could see that he wasn't joking. There was a seriousness to his voice that I hadn't heard before. "Are you talking about the Crusades?"

"Of course," he said. "We need to keep the fight alive. Look at this cross," he said, holding up a weathered cross necklace. "It is a family relic. My ancestors fought and died for us in the Crusades, and I will continue their mission until all of them are dead."

"All of them who?" I said. "You can't be talking about the Yemeni...about my friends." My head was spinning. "My life is here, and the people here made me feel at home. We pray to the same God, we are all the same, good and bad...."

"Don't blaspheme!" he shouted, cutting me off.

"Blaspheme? Are you hearing what you are saying? This is not the Middle Ages..."

"It's too late," he said. "They've already brainwashed you."

"You can't mean that. Yemen has a lot of bad, but it has way more good. We have so much to learn from here. The people I have met are the best, most good-hearted people on earth."

"Will you keep saying that the day they kill your sons and rape your daughters?" he said. "We need to kill them before they have the chance." He continued talking, but I couldn't hear a word he said. I just stared at him, utterly repulsed.

"Get out," I finally said, pushing him towards the door. It would be a while before the armored car returned to pick him up, but I had no intention of letting him wait inside. I could see the fear in his eyes as I closed the door. When I could no longer hear the echo of his footsteps, I slid to the floor and began to cry.

Adventure 5
The Diplomat

CHAPTER 34

Club Istanbul had become the gathering spot for an atypical mixture of NGO workers waiting to be evacuated, lonely freelance journalists, thirsty contractors and dodgy businessmen. Most of the expat community had left, private companies, United Nations, and international NGOs had evacuated non-essential staff, and most essential staff didn't leave their compounds. With all the drama going on in the country, our weekly Thursday night dance party felt like group therapy.

That night, I didn't care who was at Club Istanbul, or what had brought them there, or who they were staring at, even if the one they were staring at was me. It was in this state of abandon that I felt a presence at my side. I turned to see a man dancing from a cautious distance. He looked to be in his mid-forties, neat and dressed impeccably in a tailored suit with polished shoes. The song ended, and he walked over to me.

"May I know your name, before I ask you for a dance?"

Maybe it was the fact that I did not care about anything that day, maybe it was the whiskey running through my veins, or maybe there was something about him that felt right. Whatever it was, I surprised myself when I replied with my real name.

"A pleasure to meet you," he said offering a polite handshake.

We danced to a couple of songs. He was a good enough dancer, easy to dance with, not too close, not too far, good rhythm...even a couple of interesting moves.

"You're too good, I cannot follow your beat," he said. I smiled. "Do you want to sit for a while?"

I followed him to his table where we joined a young man I learned was his colleague. They worked together at the Jordanian embassy. The colleague was funny and talkative. As the young man talked, I took a closer look at the man I'd been dancing with. He had aged well, like a good wine, a sexy older gentleman. But the most attractive thing about him was his aura of self-confidence and kindness. Anna spotted us and sat down, no doubt as much for the bottle of whiskey on their table as for the company. The conversation cheered up, and when they asked me about my work, we came to know our offices where only a couple of streets apart.

We danced a bit more that night, but that was it. Our driver had arrived, and it was time for Anna and I to leave. After refusing his offer to drive us back, we exchanged phone numbers and I left. I wondered if he would call me.

The following week he called to offer me a ride to my office, since we were "office neighbors". It was the perfect excuse, and my designated taxi hadn't come to pick me up yet. Maybe it was luck, maybe it was meant to be. A few minutes later, I slipped into the black leather seat of his Porsche Cayenne. He looked surprised when I handed him some Belgian chocolates as a thank you gift for the favor. He seemed delighted by the gesture. Sitting in the office, I resisted all morning, but by the afternoon, I couldn't help myself. I sent him a text.

Hi office neighbor. How is your day going at the other side of the street?

It just got better with this text. All chocolates eaten by my colleagues though.

Do you need a refill? I will send a packet down the street.

Sweet, but I prefer to pick it up myself.

It was the first of a long series of texts over the week that followed. I felt like a spy, sending covert humor into his otherwise serious office via text messages that made him laugh. From the moment I'd met him, I'd felt comfortable by his side. The more we talked, the more drawn I was to him. He knew how to deal with people, and people treated him with respect. He had charisma, manners, and power, but more than all of those things, he was filled with genuine kindness. After our weeklong banter, he invited me to lunch. Not a suspicious late dinner or drinks at his place after hours, but lunch, which made me more nervous than I'd been since arriving in Yemen.

He picked me up at the office gate and we went to a stylish fish restaurant. The first thing he did was apologize for being a bit late. "I'm sorry to make you eat your lunch at 14:00," he said.

"No worries, I am used to eating at this time, never before 13:30," I said lightly. "You have nothing to apologize for."

"But still, a woman like you should never be kept waiting," he said, looking down. "I have a confession."

"Oh?" I said.

"That night, when we first met in the club? That was the first time I've ever approached someone in that way."

"Well, very lucky for you," I laughed. "It was also a first for me."

"How so?" he said, leaning forward.

"I have never actually given my name, let alone my number, to someone who approached me for a dance."

"Thank God for beginner's luck," he said, his voice dancing with humor.

"Yes," I said, staring at him boldly.

We sat happily removing the heads off our shrimp and spines from fresh fish until we were completely full and late for our respective offices. Like a good gentleman, he drove me back to the office without further proposition, but the chemistry we had when we first met had been amplified. I could tell we both felt it.

Do you know that feeling when you go to a shop and find the perfect dress? Exactly the one you imagined? Or when you find that job that exactly matches your expertise? When you find the man who has everything you didn't know you wanted, it feels something like that. It was as effortless as slipping on that dress.

We never intended to be friends and we never treated each other as such. It was a relationship from minute one. He treated me like a lady, like his lady. He was my Don. In the short space of three weeks we became inseparable and there wasn't a single day we didn't see each other. However, that first lunch was one of the last times we would be alone in public. Without me even realizing it, we met for shisha, coffee, and dinners, but always with a few of his friends. I didn't mind, and it seemed that neither did he. I was content and happy as our relationship continued along at hyperspeed.

My curiosity grew as the best tables were offered to us at every restaurant we entered. We were always taken to the private or VIP areas of the shisha cafés. And everyone we met seemed to greet him like he was a celebrity. I don't tend to pose many questions, preferring to allow people to open up at their own pace, the same way I like to do. But, after a particularly over-the-top greeting one night, it seemed too obvious a question not to ask.

"Everyone seems to know you," I said teasingly. "What exactly is it that you do at the embassy?"

He looked down shyly before he answered in a soft voice. "I'm the ambassador."

CHAPTER 35

"What?" My mouth dropped open. Any other person would have shouted his powerful title from the rooftops, but his humility made him sound almost embarrassed. It made me adore him even more, but I felt a knot of dread in my stomach. Some women might have jumped from happiness imagining all the power, money, and connections the man in front of them had, but I had a feeling that his position would bring more trouble than advantage.

"You look shocked."

"I am a little bit...quite a lot, actually," I said. I felt so naïve, so clueless. "Why have you never mentioned it before?"

"A lot of people approach me because of my position and my connections. You were different, and I didn't want to change that."

An awkwardness lingered as we finished our coffees, I thought I knew this man, but I knew nothing about him. I wondered if our magic was broken, but our relationship only seemed to intensify after his revelation. There was no shisha he smoked without me, or horse-riding session (his favorite pastime) that I missed. He filled my days with small surprises: flowers, boxes of chocolates and sweets, private cars coming to pick me up. But they came along with fake promises to go here or there, or that he would show me this or that. I began to see that the only time we were alone was in his house, and when we were out, we were surrounded by the same small circle of his close friends.

One night as we drove home, passing by a well-known restaurant, he brought it up again. "Have you been to this restaurant? The place is very elegant inside".

"Is it? I've never tried" I said.

"I wish I could take you there, you and me"

"So, let's go," I said. "We have never dined out alone the two of us."

"I wish, but you know how Yemen is...in this conservative society if someone at my level shows up with a woman he is not married to, rumors and gossips will spread in no time and I don't want to face problems, better to stick to their rules."

And I believed him that it was just a matter of appearances. I believed him because I wanted to. Yet, despite being cautious, gossip did spread. Often when I entered cafes and restaurants, I heard whispered references to "Bint Al Urduni" the girl of the Jordanian. I tried to ignore it. To me, the Don was not the big man they knew. He was the sweet, shy man I seduced with a silly box of Belgian chocolates.

One day, the Don was running late, so he sent his driver to pick me up. We had plans to meet at our favorite coffee shop, located on the only posh street in Sana'a. I arrived to find two of his colleagues, who had become my friends, sitting at a big round table in the corner. It was a bit cold, so I broke from tradition and ordered a hot chocolate. After we'd exchanged our usual chit chat, I took the opportunity to use the free Wi-Fi and reply to some pending emails, and the guys went back to speaking to one another in Arabic.

"Wife..." I looked up from my typing. The Arabic word had jumped out at me. I knew neither of them were married, and I wondered who they were talking about. I looked back down at my screen and tried to listen more carefully. "The Don, he is late again," one of them said, shaking his head. "It's Sunday, so he must be on the phone with his wife, or maybe his little son or daughter."

It is not forbidden for ladies to drive in Yemen. Not many do, particularly in the capital, but you will occasionally see one. Most female drivers in Yemen don't have a driving license. No police officer will stop them to check it, so why should they bother to get one? They are typically quite dangerous on the road, with no regard for posted signs or general directions of traffic flow, much like their male counterparts. In Yemen, it is most common to drive very slowly and not to look behind or to the sides, instead focusing straight ahead with no neck movement. At all. I call it static driving. And for women, there is an added obstacle, that Anna firsthand discovered.

At some point, Anna got it in to her mind that she wanted to drive. She had a license back in her home country and was an experienced driver. She asked some of our Yemeni friends if she could use their cars, a request which they all politely, and awkwardly, denied. One of our most honest friends, finally gave her an explanation.

"*Mashnouna!* Do you want my car to get shot at?" he asked. "I am still paying the installments for it! A foreign lady driver is sure to draw a lot of attention."

Still, given her stubborn streak, I had no doubt that sooner or later, Anna would succeed in her mission.

One afternoon we were having coffee with a Yemeni friend in our house. He'd made the critical mistake of driving over in his own car. "Did you come by car?" Anna pounced.

"Yes, did you want me to take you somewhere?" he politely asked.

"Oh!" she groaned. "You cannot imagine how much I miss driving these days!" Anna had started her irresistible convincing strategy.

"I didn't know you drive," he said brightly.

"Yes, and I love it so much and it would make me so happy to drive here in Yemen," she said. "Even if it is only for one day, even for half an hour."

"Aha..." he said, taking a long sip of his coffee.

"Would you be so kind as to let me go drive with you?" she asked, giving him puppy eyes. I watched, waiting for her to launch her next offensive in the campaign. "You would make me so happy," she said, leaning closer.

"Maybe..." he said, squirming.

"Could we go now?" she asked with crocodile tears in her eyes.

Our friend looked at me for help. I shrugged. If Anna wanted to drive, I figured it was better that she drove with him than with some random, crazy taxi driver she convinced on her way somewhere. "Ok, but only if you wear full *niqab*."

"Me too! I am coming," I shouted. An adventure! I couldn't miss that.

"Both of you, then, I don't want to see anything but black fabric."

Anna and I rushed to grab our Batman capes and Zorro masks and headed outside. She sat in the driver's seat and my friend sat in the front next to her. Anna started the engine and off we went, tearing down the lateral streets until we reached the main road.

Anna was good. Really good.

"Oh my God, oh my God, I cannot see anything with the niqab on!" she shrieked. "It's so hard to drive without lateral vision!"

She zipped around a corner and barely missed one of the street food carts selling prickly pears.

"I think men should wear one too. There would be less accidents, everyone would only look in the same direction."

She bypassed a minibus almost scratching its side.

"Ya Hayauan! Go fast, you are on my way!" she started to scream at the taxi in front of us. "The advantage of driving here is that when you scream at the other drivers, no one recognizes you!" She laughed like a madwoman. "I like this Zorro mask...! *Kess Ikhtak!* I was first, don't you know how to drive?"

She passed yet another car.

"Get out of my way, *ya sharmout!*"

Anna was creating havoc in the streets of Sana'a.

All the Yemeni drivers we crossed paths with must have explained over dinner how they had managed to save their cars and lives from the crazy lady driver they had encountered that evening on their drive home. We reached home after dark. Anna had cursed her quota for the whole year and was fully convinced that drivers worldwide should wear blinders to reduce the accident rate.

CHAPTER 36

I didn't want to believe what I'd just heard. But there was no denying it. I had fully understood. They kept talking, completely unaware I had eavesdropped on their conversation regarding their dear friend, convinced it was safe to talk in their language in front of me. My mind reeled. There was a wife and a family somewhere far from Yemen that existed in the Don's life.

"I have somewhere I need to be," I said, standing and shoving my laptop in my bag. I handed a few crumpled bills to the waiter for my hot chocolate.

"No need to pay, you were at his table," the waiter protested.

"Keep it," I said and rushed out of the shop. I walked right past the Don's driver, who waited for me at the door, and climbed into a taxi.

A half an hour later, the Don called. I ignored the ringing. He called again. I didn't answer. I knew that no one refused calls from the Don. You simply don't ignore big fish in Yemen if you want to stay out of trouble, but I didn't care. When he called again hours later. I wrote back a single word. Busy. Two days later, my phone rang. It was the Don. I suddenly wondered why I was the one hiding from him, when he was the liar. I answered and agreed to see him.

Adorned in my nicest *abbaya*, high-heel shoes, and expertly drawn tiger eye make-up, I completed my look with my best poker face. I slid into the passenger seat of his car and smiled my most convincing fake smile. "I feel like having shisha, why don't we go to a café?" I asked, testing him and knowing there was no way he would be seen with me alone in public.

"I have the perfect shisha flavor at home," he said. "It's a new one, we can have shisha there."

"No, let's go somewhere outside the house just for a change," I insisted, knowing he didn't like to be pushed. "I want to see some fresh faces."

"I wouldn't mind, but you know the people here..." he said. "We can go later with the guys."

I felt the heat rising to my cheeks. I had assumed we couldn't be seen out together because we were not married, but it was precisely because he was. Just not to me. We arrive at his enormous villa and sat facing one another in the living room.

"You look beautiful today," he said.

"Only today?"

"Always," he laughed, leaning closer to kiss my cheek. I turned away. "Is there something wrong?"

"Tell me, how are you today?" I asked, looking in his eyes, unsmiling.

"I'm okay, thanks..."

"And your son and daughter? How are they?" I asked, watching him carefully as he sat back.

He paused for a moment before he answered. "They are also okay," he said.

"Your wife, too? All good with her?"

"How do you..."

I put my hand up to stop him. "Now you know what's wrong."

Flying High

IN YEMEN

I was never afraid of flying until I took a trip to Socotra. Bilma and I went on vacation to this paradise island in the very south, almost at the horn of Somalia. Though the land belongs to Yemen, Socotra is a world apart. It is an island of white sand beaches and crystalline water, and of the magnificent mushroom-shaped dragon's blood tree. Socotris, ethnically different from Arabs, speak Mahari, the same language found on the border between Yemen and Oman. The cutest thing in the island is that men greet each other with a nose rub. And the best part is that it is completely empty of people aside from a few little fishing villages here and there.

While we were in Socotra, we didn't need to cover. We swam in our bikinis, slathered in sunscreen. We cooked lobster and fresh fish on the beach for breakfast. And at night, when it was too hot to sleep inside the tents, we laid on the sand, where little white crabs beat our bare feet with their claws and made us dream we were being tickled. It was paradise.

After camping for seven days and six nights, climbing white dunes and racing dolphins in fishermen boats, it was time to head back to Sana'a. Bilma had extra vacation days, so she decided to stay behind for a little longer with a family in one of the villages. I arrived at the airport and was met by the friend who had helped us organize the trip. My flight was overbooked, but, fortunately, he knew everyone in the island, including the pilot of my flight, who agreed to take me back to Sana'a.

It seemed like the perfect ending to the perfect week. I waited in a nice VIP section that had cold air-conditioning and hot tea. It felt luxurious compared to the nomad island where I'd spent the previous week. My friend was on the phone and after some minutes, he walked proudly towards me grinning.

"I have a surprise for you," he said. "You will fly in the cockpit, like a real copilot!"

"Really?" I shrieked, trying to contain my excitement. "I've never been in a cockpit before!"

"Baharoon," he said, waving at the older man who was followed closely by a young, serious looking guy.

"So, you are the lady who will help us pilot today, aren't you?" the pilot said in a perfect English accent. "Let's get to it." He winked and I followed him past security, past the lines, and directly to the plane.

Pilot and copilot took their seats and closed the door. They unfolded a semi-chair behind them. I could lean approximately half my butt on the surface. They strapped me into the tiny seat with heavy belts.

"Do you want some tea or coffee?" the copilot asked.

"Yes, please," I said, smiling at him. "Coffee would be good."

He spoke into a walkie talkie and a stewardess appeared with two big lattes and a beer.

"Thanks sweetie," Baharoon said, handing the copilot and I our lattes and cracking open his beer.

"First time I've seen non-alcoholic beer in a can," I mentioned.

"This is not exactly non-alcoholic," he said conspiratorially. "We fly to Dubai once a week and enjoy the benefits of the duty-free. Call it advantages of the pilot's life!" He chuckled and took a long swig. "I like to have a beer before starting the flight, it relaxes me while the crowd is getting on the plane. Passengers can be so noisy and annoying sometimes, right?" he said, elbowing the copilot.

Baharoon pressed some buttons and the engines came to life. We slowly started rolling down the runway. "Do you see that! Do you see it?" the copilot shouted. "There's a group of gazelles there, in the lane!"

Baharoon pulled some levers, and the plane angrily rolled to a stop. I could see a heard of the lovely animals quietly enjoying the sun on the asphalt of the landing strip. "Well, I can't do anything about them," he said, getting comfortable in his seat. "We will wait until they leave."

With a hundred passengers onboard, we sat and chatted while waiting for twelve gazelles to finish sunbathing. Just when I didn't think I could find another thing to ask to Captain Baharoon and his copilot, the gazelles began moving towards the forest. We roared down the runway and were airborne in minutes. The view was so amazing from the cockpit. I could see the mountains and beaches and the immense deep blue ocean. We climbed higher until we were above the clouds. "This is magnificent," I said.

"Yes, and only one thing could improve it," the copilot said. "Do you smoke shisha?"

"Yes ..." The question caught me by surprise.

"Perfect, then it will not bother you if I smoke," he grinned. "We can share. Apple flavor is good for you?"

I started laughing. "Shisha in a cockpit? Can you imagine?" I said, my words fading into a mumble as I watched him pull a towering shisha pipe from behind his seat. "I thought it was forbidden to smoke on planes..."

"Oh, no worries, in here it is allowed," said Baharoon, who calmly lit a cigarette. "Pilot's life."

The copilot, who had finished preparing his shisha, was working on lighting a piece of barbecue coal.

"Enjoy the shisha," Baharoon nodded. "I prefer cigarettes with my qat." My eyes bulged as he pulled out a bag of leaves.

"You see, one thing we cannot prepare in here is real charcoal, but the barbecue ones work pretty well too..." the copilot explained. "It gets a bit smoky, but you get used to it after some time."

"No worse than a chewing room in Sana'a," shrugged Baharoon. "And did you see this view?" Yemenis adore chew qat on the top of mountains as the drug seems to enhance the view. "This is a million-dollar view!" he exclaimed. "Here, take some," he handed me a full bag of qat.

I was paralyzed, watching them smoke and chew. I couldn't decide if I should spend the rest of the flight praying for my safety and cursing the pilots for their irresponsibility, or if I should give in and enjoy the astonishing views and chew the premium qat sitting on my lap. I decided on all of the above. I chewed and prayed and gasped at the stunning views, and cursed the men smoking and laughing with a hundred lives in their hands.

As we began our landing, I wondered if we would arrive in one piece or in pieces. We hit the tarmac with a thud and I heard the passengers cheer. If only they knew. Better that they didn't. Now, whenever I take a flight, I can't help but wonder in terror what's happening in the cockpit.

CHAPTER 37

"Come on, let's go dance!" Anna begged. "They are all missing you, Club Istanbul is not the same without you".

"I'm tired," I said. It was true I was tired. I was tired of wolves, of unwanted attention, and of all parasites who just wanted to suck my blood.

"How can you be tired?" she pushed. It was a total role reversal for us, since I was usually the party-lover and Anna the lazy-ass, but since my last conversation with the Don, and few weeks out of the country on a timely work trip, I hadn't shown my face in public. Being away felt like a breath of fresh air, but all I had pushed aside caught up with me upon my return.

"Anna, I am not coming to Club Istanbul, I have to finish some work. And it is not safe," I said.

"Since when do you care about that?" she asked

"Since I stepped out of this country for two weeks and realized how fucked up things are here. Cars shouldn't explode by our side Anna, we shouldn't need to cover up head to toe not to be identified and hunted. This is crazy"

"Liar, you don't care about that. You are only hiding from your married blue prince," Anna and her comments, always directly to the wound.

"Just say hi to everyone for me and have fun! You look amazing in those red trousers..."

After Anna left, I baked a cake I didn't taste and tried to watch a movie, which I shut off even before the battery on my computer died. I asked myself for the millionth time how could I have been so stupid to have believe him. It was the same story repeating again, just like the first time I had fallen for a man in Yemen. I should have stuck to my original plan, all those years ago. If I had continued my strike, I could have avoided so many disasters, and so much heartache.

Outside of Yemen, I had been simply one more grey shadow in a human landscape, an invisible girl, In Yemen, I felt like honey for flies. *"Too many butterflies around you my dear, too many butterflies! Just remember, as pretty as they are, they're still insects!"* Bilma had told me once. I missed her.

As I began to fall asleep, around 11 p.m. on a party evening, I promised myself I would stick to this nun-like lifestyle. I just wanted to stay home, alone and depressed, and with no men within a 10km radius. I woke up with the first sunlight and the call to prayer. The singer's voice was modified by the metallic loudspeakers. Such a pity his beautiful call was destroyed in such a way. Technology can be evil sometimes, even if used for the sake of religion. I imagined the smell of coffee and jumped out of bed to prepare myself a well-deserved latte. I was trying not to make much noise since Anna would be sleeping in her room. The coffee machine was buzzing. I added the milk and the foam and made a heart decoration with chocolate powder to treat to myself. I was glad she was still asleep. I didn't want to know anything about her party the night before. I had decided to stay away from everyone and all the fake theater they were playing their parts in.

My lips were about to savor the first sip of my latte when a gust of wind and the slam of the door announced Anna's entrance. "Guess who I found yesterday," she said before I'd taken my first sip. "And guess who asked for you?"

"I have no idea, and I prefer not to know," I said.

"Are you sure? Because he was very glad to know you are back in town," she said and sat straight in front of me at the kitchen table.

"He asked me a lot of questions about you"

"Whoever it is I am not interested, and I hope you didn't tell anyone anything about me..."

"The Don," she blurted out.

"Annaaaaaa!" I moaned. "Please, I said I didn't want..."

"We were checking some pictures of you on the phone and talking so much about you..."

"How could you show him my pictures, Anna?" I was getting madder at her by the second.

"He showed me first his shisha collection of pictures with you, so cute you two!"

"I'm serious, I don't want to know anymore." I stood up and heading for the kitchen's door.

"He misses you a lot, I can tell," she said in a serious tone.

"Then he will continue to miss me, because I have zero intentions of seeing him or anyone else in this country, and I'm not going out, so you can stop asking."

CHAPTER 38

After two more extremely boring weekends home, I could no longer stand to be in the house. If faith can move mountains, boredom can move entire ranges. So that Thursday night, after a little unnecessary convincing by Anna, I agreed to join her at Club Istanbul.

When we arrived, two Turkish contractors waved us over to their table. I knew they weren't the best company, but it was better to sit with them and avoid other parasitic butterflies. The taller one was Anna's biggest admirer and a decent enough guy, though his friend was generally a pretty disgusting person, even more so when drunk. I abandoned him in the middle of his indecipherable drunk babble and headed to the dance floor. Anna followed me, no doubt knowing I wasn't in the best mood, and wanting to keep me company. I was dancing mechanically, pretending to have some fun, hoping no one could decipher my real state of mind. As we danced, I saw movement at the door, and there he was.

The Don entered the club with a stunning blonde and another Arab man who was accompanied by a not-so-hot-but-still-spicy blonde. "Ha," I choked out an angry laugh. The man who refused to be alone with me in public for months had the nerve to hang out with two spicy blonds on a crowded Thursday night. I wondered what had happened to caring about his reputation, to his portrait of perfect husband. I fixed an icy, elegant smile on my face and nodded a greeting to the Don from a distance. He looked unusually disconcerted. His eyes darted between me and his date, and he seemed suddenly aware of her and his hypocrisy. I kept my eyes fixed on them, unflinching.

When they arrived on the dance floor with their blonds, he walked straight to me. "Do you have a moment?" he said. "I wouldn't like to interrupt..."

"Of course," I said, smiling as sweetly as I could manage.

"I would like to present to you my friend Dina. Do you know each other?"

She looked at me blankly. It was clear she didn't expect the Don to introduce her to the *Bint al Urduni.* I held my head up confidently.

"Nice to meet you Dina," I said, softly shaking hands with her. "We never had the pleasure to be introduced before."

She was a sexy in a way I am not, but I had class and good manners, qualities that my grandmother instilled in me as she tried to convert me into a "real" lady. I knew the Don found those qualities more appealing than any others. I continued dancing on my own, but after a couple songs I returned to the table and pretended to enjoy a conversation with the drunken Turks. I'd had enough for one night. I whispered to Anna that I was leaving, and I called my taxi before handing my coat check ticket to the waiter and asking him for my bill. He reappeared moments later with my Batman cape and an empty envelope.

"Your bill has been paid, Miss," he said, turning and nodding his head towards the Don. I took the envelope where my bill was supposed to be and placed a couple of notes inside.

"Please, give this to Monsieur," I said, handing it to him.

As I put my *abbaya* on, I watched the waiter deliver the envelope. No one else in the club knew what is going on between us. No one has seen him paying my bill or me repaying him. An offering, a rejection, our little fight

217

hidden and discrete. Just the way we both preferred it. By the time the Don lifted the envelope to look inside, I was already through the exit door.

It was over. He knew it, and I knew it. I would never see him again.

THE DYING TRADITIONS OF

Yemeni Souks

Walk around the souk of old Sana'a in the early morning and ask for half a kilo of salt in the first shop in the long line of spice sellers. Much to your surprise, it might happen that although you see a big bag of the white substance behind him, he will tell you that he has none. Go to the second shop, and the same thing will happen. Try the third, the fourth, until you reach the fifth shop. In there you will finally find a grinning old man, willing to sell you your cooking must-have.

Why did the other four refuse to sell you a simple half kilo of salt if their shops are open and the product is in there? It's the old traditional system of trade, which has ruled the markets in all of Yemen since ancient times.

This system of trade, called the "starting of the working day," was the widely spread practice among vendors of the same kind of merchandise, which allowed all the shops to get their first sale of the day. If one of the sellers had already sold some goods to the earliest customers of the souk, and therefore, his business was considered "open", he kindly redirected his next customers to the neighboring shop, despite having the products his clients were asking for. Once this neighboring shop had made its very first sale of the day, customers were sent to a third shop. This "customer-sharing" loop was repeated until the last shop in the souk had done its own "starting of the day."

Once all businesses were open, normal competition started. However, the "starting of the day" practice created a feeling of harmony and community among all the sellers. It was transmitted from father to son, and the sellers-to-be had to learn it before opening their own shops. And new shop owners had to respect it and transmit it, and so on. This practice was highly rooted in the life of traders, particularly in Sana'a.

This is also one of the reasons why most Yemeni markets tend to be grouped by the product they offered. Take, for example, the Spice Market in old Sana'a. As if drawn with a set-square, it is difficult to imagine a more precise distribution of shops by product. Although it is commonly agreed that comparison of prices and quality before you buy whatever object you need is more than recommendable, do you really need to check eighty shops before you decide on which one you are going to buy something from?

"You scratch my back, I'll scratch yours" might have thought the first traders who joined together on one street to sell the same sort of goods. But if the "starting of the day" reigned over Yemeni markets for centuries, today it is in danger of extinction.

Go back on your morning walk around the market, this time to the street full of fruit shops that run from the city walls to the main square. Much to your surprise, every shopkeeper will try to catch your attention and convince you he has the best produce. Bargaining will be expected to get an acceptable price, and verbal fights among sellers to get you into their shops will be the norm rather than the exception. The feeling of community and neighborhood are gone.

The bad economic situation Yemen has been experiencing for a long time might have contributed to it. With the devaluation of Yemen's currency, fierce competition gained territory. Moreover, Sana'a became host to large number of newly arrived people migrating from all corners of the country as numerous salesmen relocated their shops to Sana'a hoping to benefit from the concentration of businesses in the capital. The city expanded, and the neighbors started to cross unfamiliar faces walking in the streets and opening new businesses.

The feeling of belonging became blurry and the community affiliations started to dissipate. Why should a newly-arrived owner wait for his unknown competitors to start their business for the day if he has the opportunity to sell now? Why should a long-ago settled vendor allow a recently-established seller, who is not part of the centuries-old group of families in the business, to open his business before his peers?

Thus, the "from bad to worse" economic situation in Yemen, combined with the loss of traditional community links, proved to be a lethal combination for the traditional system of norms ruling the Yemeni markets. New people and new economic realities brought new practices — more practical, more individualistic.

However, in some markets, the "starting of the day" persists, and the traditional system of "fair business" is still in practice. The spice market in old Sana'a is one of the best examples of it. Same product, same price. You can waste your time asking shop after shop, but the answer to your "how much?" will be the same.

"My great-grandfather opened this shop a long time ago. He taught my grandfather how to behave with his neighbors and how to start the business day every day, early in the morning, after reading the Koran together inside the shop," explained the owner of the spices and natural remedies shop on one of the edges of the market. "My grandfather taught my father, and he taught me. We have all followed this practice. I will also teach my son and with God's will, he will also follow this practice."

"We all know each other here," adds his neighbor, speaking from behind his little shop, packed to the top with cinnamon sticks and cardamom. "We are all neighbors and we help each other. We have to be fair in business."

If you go to the market early in the morning, but not too early, you can listen to the cordial greetings between neighbors. In the spice market, at least for a little while, you can still hear the old man in the first shop say: "I'm sorry, I don't have salt. Try next door."

CHAPTER 39

Anna and I were trying to hold on to some sort of normal life, but it became increasingly difficult to ignore the fact that each time we stepped out onto the street, we were in danger. We were almost in a full lockdown, barely leaving the house. We were working from home and instead of shopping on our own, we called the grocery store and the fruit shop in our neighborhood and asked them to deliver. Anna managed to convince me a few times to go out for shisha and coffee, even though the coffee shops were emptier than ever. There, we never removed our Zorro masks, so only the waiters who already knew us would recognize who we were. We started entering buildings from the back doors, never the main entrances, but then I stopped. It was not worth the risk.

After several weeks of confinement, the walls were closing in. Anna was struggling staying indoors.

"Anna, please, don't sneak out for walks anymore," I began our nearly daily argument. "Even if you are fully covered with *niqab*, people can tell you are a foreigner."

"I didn't come to Yemen to be closed at home like a hamster in a cage."

"Then take the next evacuation flight and leave."

"Says the one who is staying?" she laughed. "You know I'll never go. Good and bad, I love Yemen."

"Fine, just don't go far, and please be careful," I said as I helplessly watched her walk out the door.

An hour later the phone rang. My soul shattered as the nurse spoke. She had been gunned down, three shots in the back, as she walked through the diplomatic quarter. Miraculously she survived, and a minibus driver had taken her to the hospital, more dead than alive.

I called a driver and raced to ICU, my head spinning. Why her? Why the woman who loved Yemen more than any of the rest of us, the one who was utterly devoted to the country and its people. I wanted the injustice of it all to spark some kind of anger in me, but instead, it just broke my heart. I sat by Anna's bedside and called our friends. She was unconscious. And sitting with her made me feel more alone than I ever had. Not a single of our expat friends showed-up. No one but the Don.

He had called a few hours after I reached the hospital. "Anything I can do, I am here."

When I left the hospital, it felt natural to go directly to his home. Day after day, I robotically moved between the hospital and the Don's villa where I would spend the rest of the afternoon on his couch smoking shisha, playing chess or just watching him work on serious things while I tried to forget what I'd just seen.

We became inseparable again, but our relationship had changed. We knew we couldn't be together, but we cared too much about one another to be apart, especially during those dark days. The age difference helped us ease into a new reality in which he was more of a Godfather to me than a lover. It wasn't a time for lovers. It was no longer time for fun.

Three days after Anna was shot there was a new kidnapping. It was the second in two weeks, a Belgian NGO worker, one of the few who remained in town. Anna was finally stable enough to be transported out of the country. I knew if she had been able to remain conscious long enough, she would have still fought to stay. I sat smoking and thinking about how much things had changed. It felt like another lifetime when I'd snuck through checkpoints in a *niqab* for a weekend by the sea. I marveled at how I was able to love a place so fiercely, when it had been the scene of so much pain.

"You know nothing will happen to you, right?" the Don said, interrupting my thoughts. I offered him a little smile. He continued talking about the kidnappings. "And if, for whatever reason, anything happens to you, I will leave no stone unturned until I find you and bring you back to where you are sitting right now, next to me."

I knew he was serious. I had no doubt he would use all his connections to pull me out of harm's way. I had a feeling he had already started using his immense power and vast network of connections to protect me. I wasn't afraid. Unlike Anna, I still had a choice, and I was exactly where I wanted to be.

CHAPTER 40

The Don's driver picked me up in the black Cayenne instead of the usual silver car. It was grocery day, once every two weeks. After seeing only my home and the Don's living room for over 14 days, I was eager to get out, if only for fruit shopping and other small errands. We started at the fruit shop, then we picked up my laundry, and against the will of my poor driver-bodyguard, I insisted we stop for coffee. A small supermarket on the way back home would be our final stop.

I sat in the middle seat in the back of the car speaking to my boss's secretary trying to arrange some meetings. Since I had started to work from home, I was on the phone constantly trying to keep projects moving. We passed a wide street with three lanes, taking a second deviation on our left. We turned down a narrow street and I felt the driver speed up. I hung up and leaned forward to ask why he was taking a different route when he slammed on the breaks. I looked up and saw a white pickup truck blocking our way. Two men stepped out of the car holding guns. The driver threw Porsche in reverse and accelerated, I felt a crash, but he didn't break. The men start shooting and the driver jerked the wheel, scraping the side of an old building as he whipped us around and sped out of the alley. He drove without breaking all the way back to the Don's house.

He parked in the garden inside the security wall and I got out and ran my hand over the round marks the shots had left in the front and sides of the bulletproof car. The paint looked like it had been slashed by an animal. I texted the Don. *I am ok.* I knew it would not take more than two minutes for the news to reach his office and I didn't want him to worry. It was too late. My phone rang as I hit send. "Stay in my house, don't go anywhere. I am coming right now."

"No, don't..." I started to say, but he had already hung up. I wanted to tell him not to come, or to be very careful. It was clear that someone was after him, not me. I had been in his usual car. The twelve minutes it took him to reach the villa were some of the longest minutes of my life. My mind raced. What if they were waiting for him somewhere else? Would they try to attack him again on the same day, before their opportunity was lost?

In the growing nightmare of political, tribal and armed group rivalries, the Don had become a very valuable ally to a lot of people. He had tried to stay neutral for a long time, but the country he was officially representing had too much weight in Yemen. Some had had enough of his neutrality, and they were determined to force him to decide who he would support, and by extension, who he would oppose. Very powerful people were about to become enemies, and some had likely already tried to eliminate him as a threat.

I let out a quiet sob as he entered the room. I stood to embrace him, but he wasn't alone. The security attaché of the embassy was with him along with two bodyguards. Others had gathered in the room—the driver who saved my life, the maid with a cup of chamomile, and one of the guards who usually watched the doors at night. "Everyone out," the Don said.

When they all left, he rushed to hug me. "I am so sorry," he said.

"Thank God you are okay! I was so worried about you, they were going after you, we were in your car, please be very careful, please..."

A look of confusion flashed across his face. "Shhhtt... don't worry about anything now," he said, pulling me tighter into our embrace.

Minutes later the room again buzzed with hectic activity. Some Yemeni military and police officers arrived at the house. "I want to discover who was behind her attack, and I want to know it today. I will not go to sleep without having seen those soulless pigs in front of me," the Don shouted.

Phones rang, people arrived and left, talking, shouting, arguing, whispering. More people arrived and more people left, all wearing the same worried look. Sitting on a couch some meters away, gripping my now-cold cup of chamomile tea, I watched them as if I had entered an '80s detective movie dubbed in Arabic and Yemeni that I could not fully understand. My heart was calm. The Don was right there in front of me. He was safe. As long as he stayed in that room, I knew they could not attack him again.

The activity continued late into the night. I was taken to the Don's guestroom and when I woke up, I could still hear phones ringing and people talking in low voices. I'd seen high-ranking officials coming the day before, even a couple of ministers and some tribal leaders. This was a high-stakes game that I knew had nothing to do with me. The Don entered the room with the powerful look in his eyes that I had so long admired. The moment he closed the door behind him, the great leader became the gentle man I had come to know so well. He sat next to the bed, kissed me on the forehead and started playing with my hair. His eyes were fixed on me, but his mind was somewhere far from that room.

CHAPTER 41

A week passed, and then another. I had moved permanently into the Don's guest room, upon his order, not his request. I wasn't allowed to leave the villa, and on the rare occasions I did, I was accompanied by two of the Don's most trusted guards. I hated the fact that they were with me, when they should have been protecting the Don. I felt sick with anxiety every time he left the house. The Don had changed over those few weeks. Like a bad seed had taken root in his soul. It was guilt, the kind of guilt that destroys you from inside. I didn't understand why.

That night, he sat next to me and took my hand between his. "Do you remember the first thing I told you after the attack?" he asked.

"You said you were sorry," I said. There had been very few times that I'd heard the Don apologize, so I remembered it clearly, though it didn't seem important, considering everything else that happened that day.

"Do you remember your reply to me?" he asked. I shook my head and watched a sad smile form on his face. "You were worried about me. You thought I was the target of the attack, because you were in my car."

"Yes, of course..." I started to say.

"You were the target," he said. Time seemed to stand still as he paused. "The attack was intended to be on you, as a way get to me. You are my weak spot."

"You cannot feel responsible for it... how could you know?" I argued.

"The threat was there from the moment the protection I gave you became smaller than the danger of someone using you to pressure me. I was selfish to deny this reality. I wanted to find a way to keep you here, with me."

"Did they manage to get what they wanted?" I asked quietly.

"No. I couldn't allow them to set an example for others. No one uses my people to threaten me," he said. "If I had given in, you would have been in greater danger from anyone trying to reach me." He looked down at his hands. "But now, you need to leave."

"Why?" I asked, tears blurring my vision.

"Because I will not put you at risk again."

"This is not fair, it is on me to decide," I cried. When I saw the cold look on his face, I realized how powerless I was. In his position, it would take only one call to have my visa revoked. The past three years flashed before my eyes. The bad had been the worst, but the good moments were incomparable. After all my close calls, and all my triumphs, how could someone I cared about so deeply be the one to end it all?

"No, I don't accept this," I said.

"Tomorrow," he said, looking down at his hands. "You are leaving."

CHAPTER 42

After a sleepless night of packing, I was escorted to the car before sunrise. All I had with me were the stories I had collected over those years in Yemen and two suitcases full of clothes. Armed to the teeth, the Don's guards sat on either side of me. They were tense and ready to carry out their mission. That day, their mission was to put me on a plane to somewhere far, far away.

I stared at the villa, waiting for the Don to emerge. I wondered how I would be able to say goodbye to him. It was only as we pulled away that I realized he would not be coming. As we drove towards the airport, I watched a slideshow of memories play in the dark windows of old Sana'a. All the laughter and tears and love and fear flooded my mind. I'd seen the best and the worst of Yemen, and I still loved it so much. The guards silently walked me to my gate, and when I got onboard, I pressed my head against the window. I strained to catch every last glimpse of jagged rooftops.

Just as they had started, with a nondescript flight and no idea what lay ahead, my little adventures in Yemen were over. As the city disappeared from the oval window, I whispered, "Goodbye."

ABOUT THE CREATORS

the Author
FRANCA SOL

Franca Sol is a Middle East based writer and humanitarian worker. She has lived and worked in Oman, Lebanon, Yemen and Iraq, where she is currently based.

Her background is in Intercultural Affairs, specialized in the Middle East.

Little Adventures in Yemen is her debut novel. Get in touch at LittleAdventuresinYemen.com / @LittleYemen

the Illustrator

SARAH ALJOUMARI

Sarah Aljoumari is a Yemeni illustrator and a blogger. Sarah was born in Yemen and moved to the United States of America when she was 14 years old. Her work has a broad popular appeal among Yemeni Americans through Instagram for their reflection of both Yemeni and American cultures.

Follow her on Instagram @s.jamjam.

the Editor

FELICIA CAMPBELL

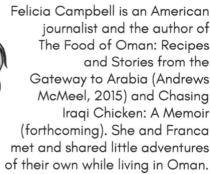

Felicia Campbell is an American journalist and the author of The Food of Oman: Recipes and Stories from the Gateway to Arabia (Andrews McMeel, 2015) and Chasing Iraqi Chicken: A Memoir (forthcoming). She and Franca met and shared little adventures of their own while living in Oman. Felicia loves helping other writers tell their stories and she works with authors around the world as a developmental editor, consultant, and writing coach.

Learn more about her at feliciacampbell.com

Acknowledgments

I cannot express enough thanks to my friend Felicia Campbell. Without her magic edits and immense support, the Absolutely (Un)True Stories from Sana'a would have remained untold. Her enthusiasm, energy and professionalism made this book a reality.

Also, a very special thanks to "Anna" for her constant support through the years. Without her beautifully stubborn reminders and encouragement, Little Adventures in Yemen would not have been possible.

Finally, a sincere thanks to Yemen and its people, for all that it taught me and all the love it gave.

Lightning Source UK Ltd.
Milton Keynes UK
UKHW020435160321
380388UK00007B/695

9 788409 243983